SURRENDERING YOUR SURVIVAL

A Conscious Path to
Eating Disorder Recovery

ROBIN PHIPPS WOODALL

NOTE: Women and men both experience issues stemming from body image, diet, and struggle with emotional eating and eating disorders. For convenience, we primarily used *she/her* throughout.

DISCLAIMER

The author, Robin Phipps Woodall, is not formally trained or educated in psychology, and is not a licensed counselor or therapist. She is not qualified to diagnose and treat eating disorders. However, she does have personal experience suffering with an eating disorder—and with recovery. The author's intent is to share her thoughts, observations, and what she's studied on the matter in hopes that others might benefit.

CONTACT

If you'd like to work with Robin directly or would like to provide the *Thin Supremacy* series of books in your clinic or recovery center, email Robin directly.

Email: robin@mindbodyhcg.com

Website: www.weightlossapocalypse.com

Dedication

To the dark hell of eating disorder misery that I escaped over twenty years ago—I will never return—but I will never forget you. Without your narcissistic threats of abandonment, shame, worthlessness, and the inhumane demands and torture you required, I would not appreciate the liberation and freedom that I continue to experience today.

To the call of death that I experienced when I was at the darkest and most isolated space in my mind—you opened my eyes so I could admit failure and face the loss of my existence. You opened my mind to experience a new reality and a new existence. You guided me to surrender, to open my heart, and then saved me from committing suicide. You taught me the power of accepting the truth, which provides continuous freedom to this day.

To all of the people who've personally shared their eating disorder experience with me on many levels. They opened up about the truth of their wins and losses, and the vulnerable truth of their struggles. It is their humility and willingness to be honest with me and with themselves that allowed the work I do to evolve.

To the most important people in my life: My mother and father for being the most loving influence in my recovery. And my husband Mark and my children Chloe, Wyatt, and Suzanne—thank you for believing in me, and for having patience during the years I couldn't find the energy, motivation, or discipline to get this book project done

Contents

SECTION 5

Relearning How to Eat

Introduction

"Most things will be okay eventually, but not everything will be. Sometimes you'll put up a good fight and lose. Sometimes you'll hold on really hard and realize there is no choice but to let go. Acceptance is a small, quiet room."

– Cheryl Strayed, Author

Every aspect of suffering while in different states of survival mode plays an important part of human evolution. It's easy to judge these aspects of ourselves because they are truthfully miserable.

- However, without the misery of these mechanisms, what would inspire us to learn and evolve outside the discomforts of these self-centered limitations?

- What would motivate us to transcend primitive defense mechanisms into a higher, more-open state of mind and consciousness?

I know for me, if it weren't for such horror and misery in my own suffering, I wouldn't have opened myself up to thoughts of suicide—and from there I wouldn't have questioned why my life hit such a low level of existence.

It took complete and utter failure for me to surrender my pride, to accept failure, and to open myself to the truth.

The incredible thing is that every aspect of growth is a steppingstone, with the ultimate goal being to secure our primitive survival needs, and to transcend narcissistic forms of self-preservation into the open life of experience, exploration, and enlightenment. However, until our basic human needs are met, these higher levels of existence, and the freedom that goes along with it, won't be available.

When the vulnerability of life is accepted—and survival mode put to rest—the way our mind works is to be less self-centered, biased, and self-promoting, and to be more open-minded and exploratory. This is what I thought I'd get when I pursued weight loss. However, I ended up with a vicious cycle of survival-mode, and all-or-nothing insanity. Seeking approval and belonging through the desirability of body image required that I diminish my access to food. Inevitably, as one survival need threatened a bigger more important survival need, my mind warped, ultimately presenting itself as a paranoia of food, obsessive body image, and eventually an eating disorder.

I believe...

- Today, after working with hundreds of people on the entire spectrum of disordered eating and eating disorders, I believe *issues with food are just a symptom*, projected out from mechanisms meant to protect life, coming from the desire to "fit in" and feel lovable through body image. This is discussed in my book, *Thin Supremacy: Body Image and Our Cultural Battle with Weight.*

- I believe the cognitive distortions about one's body and food, like dysmorphia, perfectionism, and all-or-nothing thinking, are from a clash between the psychological drive to belong, fit in, and be accepted—and the more vital, more important need to survive with food. This is discussed in my book *Diet Supremacy: The Toxic Bond Between Shame, Dieting, and Emotional Eating.*

- I believe people who suffer with an eating disorder hold themselves to abusive and inhumane controls—like someone with Stockholm Syndrome—because they believe that's what they have to do to earn safety, acceptance, and love from the narcissistic supremacy (their captor) that has power and control over her survival needs. This is discussed in my book *Body Supremacy: Exploring the Torment of Eating Disorders as a Syndrome*

These three books that I call the *Thin Supremacy* series, were written as a way to observe eating disorders from evolutionary psychological perspective. Each book doesn't give instructions on what to do, but rather they were

3

written to help you understand how the mind gets warped and twisted into a radical state of survival mode.

Similar to what I thought, every single person I've worked with believed *that her pursuit for a thinner body and her disordered eating behavior would bring her happiness.* It gave her something she needed—whether she needed shelter, safety, self-defense, comfort, distraction, hope, something to work on, or fleeting moments of pride. However, like an abusive relationship, at some point, it became her biggest nightmare.

For someone in an insecure state of survival who feels too weak and unsuccessful to fight any more, facing fear and discussing her shame is a big deal. Facing underlying issues can be extremely frightening—and very difficult to accept. If you can see clearly what you need to do and what you need to sacrifice to get freedom, would you be willing? Would you surrender your eating disorder if the cost is accepting exactly what you don't want? That is what this book is about—the conscious decision to surrender your eating disorder survival and to come out of hiding to face vulnerable truth of the unknown. If your answer is yes, you're about to experience a very different life than the one you are abandoning.

Why I've Written These Books

At the worst state of my eating disorder, I remember being in such a dark space, and not knowing why.

- I didn't understand why I felt so controlled by behaviors that were ruining my life.

- It felt as if I didn't have clarity to express what I was experiencing.

- It was as if my voice was being choked, and my throat

forced shut, as I remained trapped inside a demonic space of hell, while living among friends, family, and life around me.

- I was in a mental cage, in complete darkness, while everyone around me lived in the freedom and the light.

Not having enough clarity to express myself was a large factor in why my suffering got to be as intense and demented as it did. When I eventually escaped that space and recovered, I felt in my heart the desire to give clarity to others who are suffering the way I did. But, at the time, I still didn't know how to explain why I'd made such shifts in awareness and gained such freedom. I thought that maybe my experience wasn't meant for me to use for others, but that it was a personal experience that was only important for me. So I put my desire to help others on a shelf, assuming that if it were meant to be, the opportunity would arise, and I'd give advice as it was asked for.

Ten years later, that opportunity presented itself. It took another ten years of studying and talking with people who were suffering before I was able to explain effectively what eating disorders are like, how they might be a possible syndrome, how they seem to stem from the privileged beliefs of thin and diet supremacy, as well as the chaos between two clashing survival mechanisms. As I looked back at my experience and understood it better from an intellectual point of view, I was able to put into words how I actually escaped. With that, my ability to coach and guide others improved.

Although, for people to escape their misery, it is 100 percent their responsibility, their humility, and their courage that is required. I point them in a direction towards freedom, and it's their conscious decision if they are ready and willing to take my advice.

My goal in writing these books is to put that advice into writing. My hope is to give a voice to those who are in that same dark state of hell...to give them words that might express feelings, impulses, and experience that they struggle to describe.

With this book and the entire *Thin Supremacy* series, people won't have to sift through thousands of videos from my YouTube channel (WeightLoss-Apocalypse) to find answers. They can take the time to study the content I've written, and digest what makes sense for their situation, at their own pace. From there, if they choose to reach out for my guidance, the honest way that I give feedback and direct people won't be so surprising.

A simple way to understand how these books work together is that the *Thin Supremacy* series is about why you feel the way you do when you have an eating disorder. They are meant to be studied for knowledge and understanding, but intellectual knowledge about eating disorders won't work for what you'll need to face on the path toward recovery. *Surrendering Your Survival* is about that path.

I describe what you'll need to sacrifice, accept, and consciously do in order to stop suffering. I wrote this book to speak to the heart of those who are inside the dark cage of their eating disorder. I've written this as if I'm sitting with you in that darkness, with compassion for why you are in such a state terror and indescribable levels of anguish, and to show you a path to escape. *Surrendering Your Survival* speaks to the suffering and terror experienced by those who are a slave to their eating disorder, and provides clarity about what it will take in order to willfully choose to surrender the eating disorder. The goal is to go into a new life that has freedom so that you can get the "do over" you've been praying for.

When you enter a new life of freedom in recovery, the goal is to learn how to eat again without the brainwashed dogma stemming from food morality and diet supremacy. The last section of this book is dedicated to the process of learning your body, learning signals of hunger and satiety, and sifting through possible dieting and emotional eating issues that might still arise.

The science I describe at the end of the book for the use of hunger, specifically the science of leptin, has been a crucial aspect in helping people realize their body is more trustworthy than a diet.

When teaching people, who were previously diet zealots, about the biological rhythms of leptin that regulate food consumption, they get further confirmation how amazing the human body is—and how inappropriate extrinsic diet regulation is. In comparison to the body's own regulatory system, outside programs that are constructed from some intellectual idea of the body, usually don't consider the body from an evolutionary physical or psychological perspective.

The use of the hunger scale and satiety scale I describe in section 3, provides a means to eat that is completely regulated by the body. If the truth of the body is going to be accepted, an honest use of hunger to guide when and how much to eat is the goal. Then freedom from having your mind fixated on your body and food can be experienced.

This freedom comes from unconditionally accepting the body you have, and accepting that you will experience injury, pain, disease, and inevitable death. Once you've accepted the life and consciousness it gives you, you are free to navigate with it, enjoy it, change directions, and evolve in your life. In recovery you are open to explore the expanse of possibility in life, rather than being closed inward, and controlled in *eating-disorder hell*.

When you are ready to surrender the misery of what you know, the choice is yours: to instead go into the expanse of freedom you know nothing about.

Hopefully this book will inspire you, give you hope, and motivate the loss and change that's needed to liberate your life so that it can be experienced in a different way.

> *"The most beautiful things in the world cannot be seen or even touched, they must be felt with the heart."*
>
> *– Helen Keller*

Introduction

The Goals of the *Thin Supremacy* Book Series

This entire series of books was originally written as one book. As I realized it was too large and covered too wide a range of complex information for one book, I decided to split the information into four parts. I published each section as its own book, in order of the first (*Thin Supremacy*), second (*Diet Supremacy*), and third book (*Body Supremacy*). These three books I call the *Thin Supremacy* series. The last section of the original book is the final book—*Surrendering Your Survival.* I see this book as the central cornerstone to the entire series—it provides the most important instructions toward recovery. The *Thin Supremacy* series is support for *Surrendering Your Survival,* and vice versa. They all work better together than they do separate.

A simple way to understand how these books work together is that the three *Thin Supremacy* series books were written as a way to observe eating disorders from an evolutionary psychological perspective, and to try to find sense in why people's relationship with their body and food can get so disordered. These books have more academic and intellectual content about eating disorders that is meant to be studied by people who are suffering, *and also by professionals who help people dealing with these issues.* However, intellect about the problem doesn't necessarily provide what's needed when it comes to letting your eating disorder go in order to get on the path toward recovery. *Surrendering Your Survival* is about letting go and getting on that path.

> ***Surrendering Your Survival: A Conscious Path to Eating Disorder Recovery*** provides directions toward escaping the torments of eating disorder hell. In this book I speak from my own understanding of the torment and suffering of an eating disorder, and from my own experience escaping and recovery from

it. I wrote *Surrendering Your Survival* to speak heart to heart with those who are inside the dark cage of their eating disorder. I articulate the survival terror experienced by those who are a prisoner to their disordered behaviors, and provide clarity about what it will take in order to willfully choose to surrender the safety that those behaviors supply. When reading this book, it will feel as if I'm sitting with you in that darkness, with compassion for why you are in such a state of terror and anguish, showing and describing the path you'll need to take in order to escape.

Surrendering Your Survival describes what will need to be sacrificed, what has to be accepted, and the price that must be paid to take the path that leads to recovery. I give the reader a look into what recovery feels like, a method guided by the body to relearn a functional way to eat, and send a message of hope to those who are seeking freedom from an eating disorder.

Thin Supremacy: Body Image and Our Cultural Battle with Weight focuses and discusses the underlying psychological mechanisms and societal belief systems that encourages people to reinforce unrealistic body images. For people who internalize these images, they are more likely to experience feelings of shame when their body is different. This shame is a primary motivation for why people diet and why people eat emotionally. I believe emotional eating issues *are just a symptom*, projected out from mechanisms meant to protect life, coming from the desire to "fit in" and feel lovable through body image.

Diet Supremacy: The Toxic Bond Between Shame, Dieting, and Emotional Eating describes the survival mechanisms that are triggered as the struggle to accept body fat promotes an anxiety-ridden conflict between dieting—and the survival urges to gain access to food and to eat in self-defense. I believe the cognitive distortions about one's body and food, like dysmorphia, perfectionism, and all-or-nothing thinking, are from a clash between the psychological drive to belong, fit in, and be accepted—and the more vital, more important need to survive with food.

Body Supremacy: Exploring the Torment of Eating Disorders as a Syndrome goes deeper into the mind and darkness of eating disorders. This book discusses the possibility that eating disorders might be more of a syndrome, where compliance is a form of self-preservation necessary to survive in narcissistic cultures where codependency and trauma bonding might be more prevalent. I believe people who suffer with an eating disorder hold themselves to abusive and inhumane controls—like someone with Stockholm Syndrome—because they believe that's what's required in order to earn safety, acceptance, and love from the narcissistic supremacy (their captor) that has power and control over their survival needs.

These books are not "light reading." The content and information presented is meant to help the reader to see things from a different point of view. For this to happen, you might need to read, study, cross reference, and reread different chapters from each book in the series. From a change in perspective, the goal is to see from a larger vantage point, to think differently, and to ask questions that might have uncomfortable answers.

If you are looking for light and easy reading, these books are not for you. If you are seeking answers, explanations and heart-felt care and concern, these books ARE for you.

SECTION I

When Safety is Dangerous

Request for my help from a very stressed-out mother whose child is suffering from anorexia and bulimia: My 16-year-old daughter has been struggling with an eating disorder for nearly two years. We've tried a variety of approaches from eating disorder clinics, including inpatient and outpatient therapy, nutritionists, counselors, you name it. It seems to be getting worse. She has been watching your YouTube videos for a couple months now, and sharing with us your different approach to recovery, and she is very confident that working with you will be the answer to recovery. She has been diagnosed with anorexia nervosa and bulimia, and lately it seems to be turning into more binge-eating disorder.

She has been trying very hard since September to find a solution and to recover. After exploring and learning about her own struggles, where they're coming from and what's driving them, she very much believes that your program will be the best approach for her, and maybe even her last hope. I've been attempting to accompany her along her recovery journey, and she has shared several of your videos with me. Through these experiences, we have both come to similar conclusions that traditional therapy approaches are not working for her, and it is beginning to make sense as to why after watching your videos and learning more about what she believes is driving her specific issues.

My daughter has expressed feeling of being so relieved after watching you help other people, and the way that you've been able to connect wanting to lose weight and thin supremacy with over-eating. We would like to know whether you work with minors, and are hoping very much that if you haven't, you might consider doing so.

Chapter I

The *Misery* of Safety, or the *Pain* of Danger

"*To know yourself as the Being underneath the thinker, the still-ness underneath the mental noise, the love and joy underneath the pain, is freedom, salvation, enlightenment.*"

– Author and spiritual guru Eckhart Tolle

I've always been afraid of heights. Even into my fourth decade of life, I continue to have a sense of danger being close to any ledge or to any abrupt change in height that might pose the risk of me falling. Even when I understand intellectually it isn't a threat, something as innocent as going up metal stairs that can be seen through, elicits feelings of danger.

I believe it all started when visiting a dam with my family when I was about five years old. One of my older teenage brothers picked me up and pretended as if he was going to throw me over the ledge. I was terrified, and that experience was definitely recorded by my mind's "danger area," as a real and relevant threat. Although it was funny to my brother, I'm certain he wasn't aware that to my animal survival brain, it wasn't a joke. I didn't connect the dots between the significance of that event to the degree of fear I experience when the possibility of free falling presents itself, until I intentionally looked at my past to understand it. Clearly, that fear is wanting me to avoid that experience again.

Despite it being an annoyance to me and a source of limitation, the physical discomfort I feel with heights is a beneficial safety mechanism. To my survival brain, it's lifesaving to prompt fear when I am near a tall ledge, because of the presumption that if I get too close, I'll be thrown or slip over the edge and die.

Through a sort of neurological angst or psychological pain, the mind suspends any vulnerable activity to instead direct conscious motivation towards doing whatever will remove the perceived source of danger.

The goal of the discomfort and torment stemming from fear is to find whatever it is that will make those feelings go away. Once the goal is met, the mind is rewarded with relief and pleasure.

Like when you are confronted by a nightmarish predator, the angst felt in recognizing impending threat promotes increased fear and a strong drive to conceal oneself. When a hiding place is found, then that fear is reduced, and relief is felt. This is what many people experience when they binge, eat emotionally, obsess over what's in his or her food, impulsively body check, or when they impulsively exercise or plan their next diet in fear of weight gain. This is covered in chapter 5, 6, and 7 in the book *Thin Supremacy: Body Image and Our Cultural Battle with Weight.*

In the case of an eating disorder:

- If bingeing on food is what hides you from the pain of feeling inadequate, seeking out food to eat is going to provide that relief.

- If restricting food is what prevents the possibility of being seen as worthless, it would be weird for you not to follow that directive.

- If puking up eaten food or impulsively exercising after you eat relieves intense and radical feelings of being exposed as a fraud or a loser, you're going to do whatever it takes to make those feelings subside.

There is reward not only in the dissipation of painful psychological impulses coming from the mind, but there's also reward in the pleasure of knowing you have something that works to effectively protect you.

Eating disorder behaviors, like obsessively measuring the body and food, are both relieving and pleasurable, but they're difficult to let go of. This is particularly true when the fear and anxiety that arises can easily and quickly be removed by simply thinking about those behaviors, like planning your next diet or what food you're going to binge on.

When experiencing fear, we aren't wired to take the time to process, question, and observe where the source of danger is coming from. That would put you in a position of being disadvantaged, if the threat is bigger, faster, and stronger than you. Our mind instinctively pivots away from the vulnerability and towards coping mechanisms that are geared to fight, hide, look away, deny, repress, or escape the discomfort as quickly as it arises.

The source of weakness and threat quickly gets hidden from the conscious mind as defense mechanisms keep your mind occupied on what will provide immediate relief. In an enabled way, you become weaker to handle and understand why you're experiencing a sense of danger, while you focus and prioritize a stronger and more positive relationship with the way you psychologically cope using your eating disorder behaviors.

> **The triggers to psychologically run, hide, shrink, and fight with eating disorder behaviors would make more sense if they were connected to clear and dangerous physical threats, such as being pushed off the ledge of a cliff or being attacked by a grizzly bear.**

But because they are coming from narcissistic beliefs that are so widely accepted about body image, perceptions of "bad" food, and the dogma that suggests diets provide the only safe way to eat, it's easy to see why people don't understand their struggle to let those destructive behaviors go.

> **IMPORTANT:** I describe narcissism as it relates to eating disorders in detail in section 2 of *Body Supremacy: Exploring the Torment of Eating Disorders as a Syndrome.*

NOTE: The mind not only responds to perceptions of physical dangers, like encountering a rattle snake, grizzly bear, drowning

18

in the ocean, or falling off a mountain ledge, it also responds to perceived psychological dangers. Examples of these dangers would be perceived threats of starvation, lack of water, environmental danger that arises when exposed to hazardous weather, as well as threats to being seen as worthless which would make a person vulnerable to being abandoned by loved ones. When these psychological threats are secured, the mind experiences the same type of relief and pleasure one would expect when successfully defending oneself from being injured and eaten by a predator, or when a person who is actively drowning in deep water find a floatation device and reaches safety on land. The needs for food, shelter, and partnership in life are just as important as gaining safety from being eating by a predator.

Evolutionary psychology suggests, as humans have evolved physically to survive the environment, we've also evolved psychologically with the drive and desire to get what we need to stay alive and to avoid death.[1] It would make sense that our minds are pre-wired with "genetic memory" to be attracted to and defensive of necessary life requirements that would improve our capacity to survive.

It's predictable that humans have some degree of insecurity when seen as inadequate or worthy of exclusion. However, based on findings, we have higher degrees of insecurity when it comes to losing shelter and environmental safety, and we are the most insecure to handle threats to food, water, shelter and other physiological necessities for life.

The innate drive and motivation of human behavior—looked at from the angle of evolutionary psychology—is largely based on the work of world-renowned scientist, Dr. Abraham Maslow (1908–1970). According to his research studying human motivation and behavior, our foremost psychological priority is to secure the most important things needed to stay alive. In terms of our innate drive to probe for danger, he believed this ability was prewired to seek any threat to the most vital physiological needs for life, like food, more so than other needs.

MASLOW'S HIERARCHY OF NEEDS

As it relates to eating disorders, it would be predictable that a person who perpetually diets or believes food is going away would suffer from chronic survival mechanisms and cognitive distortions geared to focus on food.

Maslow's observations went beyond being hunted by a tiger and chased by a bear. He observed that the loss of what's needed to survive is equally as threatening, and he eventually created a hierarchy of survival needs.

> **IMPORTANT:** I go into great detail about Maslow's hierarchy of needs in all three books of the Thin Supremacy series. However, I am more detailed in what I wrote in the first and second section in the book *Diet Supremacy: The Toxic Bond Between Shame, Dieting, and Emotional Eating.*

If the source of danger stems from a psychological trigger, it's easy for it to be obscured by the obvious supply of relief and pleasure people get from their coping behaviors. For this reason, if they end up having overuse issues because they've developed an overreliance with those behaviors, those actions are seen *as the problem*—not necessarily the triggered fear that underlies their drive to cope.

This is why people believe they have an emotional eating problem, rather than a dieting restriction problem. Or they think they have an addiction to food, when they probably have intense shame about their body fat that promotes anorexic-like strictness to dieting. When I suffered inside an eating disorder, I thought I had a bingeing and purging problem, and I never questioned why I was radically restricting food. Most people don't consciously understand or even question where their fear is arising from, as their mind gets fixated on what they feel impelled to do to get relief. This is covered in section 2 in the book *Diet Supremacy: The Toxic Bond Between Shame, Dieting, and Emotional Eating.*

One reason people struggle to stop their eating disordered behaviors is because they don't understand where their impulses to binge, purge, or starve themselves through diets come from and why those behaviors, despite their harm and destruction to life, are so gratifying. The reasons are immediately hidden by the intense and rapid impulse to do the behaviors that seem to protect you. There is no time spent "in the fear" in order to understand it.

I know I felt confused and completely enslaved by what I was impelled to do every waking moment. It took me intentionally not going to my eating disorder behaviors with the conscious goal of feeling the underlying terror to find out why it was there.

To understand this would require a person to not respond when their fear or terror arises, which would allow them to feel and describe what's going on, as well as question what they're afraid of. With anxiety and distress as intense as what I experienced, to allow it to arise felt as if I was going to die. In that state of extreme fear, suggesting a person allow it to be there in order to understand it, would be like asking them to sit with the grim reaper or to allow themselves to be pushed under water to be drowned or to be thrown off a cliff. This is why, in face of the fact that my disorder was ruining my life and that I was suffering intensely, I couldn't bear to stop. When I tried to give those behaviors up, I felt sorry for myself, as if I was a victim for having to recover.

In order to get to the source of the problem, you have to willfully surrender the relief and pleasure that arises from those behaviors, and in doing so experience the terror you've been hiding from as it arises. For me, it wasn't until I had suffered so greatly that I wanted to die, that willfully giving up the eating disorder behaviors (without being a victim) became an option.

MY EATING DISORDER EXPERIENCE: I suffered greatly with bulimia. I not only puked up food after bingeing (at my worst, 10-15 times a day), but I also would exercise to extreme measures. *When in that dark existence, at least 90 percent of my life was devoted to behaviors my mind directed me to do in order to avoid traumatic levels of terror. The need to control, organize and micro-manage food, exercise, binge, puke up food, and monitor* *my weight and size temporarily protected and prevented me from having a sense of constant terror. Those fear-based and relief-driven behaviors became central to my every waking moment.*

I was so enslaved and dedicated to the eating disorder to the point that I looked forward to falling asleep at night. That was the only time I was given a break from the misery of my survival, and I felt the only other way I could conceive mercy was to commit suicide.

What protected me and provided a sense of survival, was so miserable that I was willing to kill myself in order to make it all stop.

As I contemplated dying, I realized that if I were to give up all of my protective eating-disorder defense mechanism, there might be an alternative. Ultimately, incredible levels of danger and terror would have to be accepted if I wanted freedom.

To my survival brain, giving up the eating-disorder behaviors felt as if I was willfully allowing myself to die a horrendous death, as if I was allowing myself to be murdered. By refusing to do what my terror was demanding, I was refusing my survival as well as the immediate relief those behaviors could so easily provide.

In the end, by not doing what my brain and body were directing me to do, a disconnection to those eating disorder behaviors occurred. Like a slave being unshackled, and the prison door being opened, the opportunity for freedom presents itself.

When there is space, time, and intentional focus permitted before diving into the eating disorders behaviors, the angst of fear can be experienced.

This allows a person to understand her/himself better, and to witness that the intensity of his or her behaviors is equal to the psychological danger being experienced. This awareness is an important step in not feeling so crazy, and to have compassion for why the struggle to let go of the disordered behaviors feels like torture.

When there's a radical source of psychological pain experienced through feelings of terror, it would go against the benefits of our survival to do nothing about it. It appears you have no choice but to hide, escape, avoid, or fight the source of danger you assume will destroy your existence, *even when those defense mechanisms harm you or others around you.*

> **NOTE:** The survival mind is geared to protect one's life before anyone or anything else. It is geared to reject the vulnerability of the unknown and gravitates to what is predictable within what's already known. This impedes exploration and the vulnerability that's required for growth.

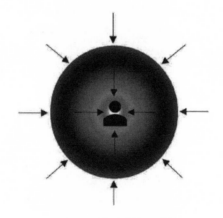

FEAR OF THE UNKNOWN

Extrinsically Controlled, Self-Centered, Defensive, Inward Focus, Codependent, Limited Life-Potential

This reminds me of a quote from spiritual guru, Deepak Chopra: *"We are prisoners of the known. Reality is always infinite possibilities in the fresh unknown."*

Fear of the Unknown

When there's apparent danger the mind shifts the perception of reality into fragments, like a shattered mirror, that distorts danger to seem bigger and more threatening than it is, and safety to seem smaller, more gratifying and important than it is. Accordingly, the mind focuses on itself, in self-defense, as a way to protect itself from danger.

In this state, a person doesn't consciously have much freedom in his or her mind because it is oriented to do what is necessary to diminish fear and relieve the physical angst of survival mode.

> Cognitive distortions are described in more detail in chapter 7, "The Mind of Survival Mode" from the book *Diet Supremacy: The Toxic Bond Between Shame, Dieting, and Emotional Eating.*

To outsiders, this appears incredibly selfish, self-centered, and egotistical… because it is. When in a heightened state of fear, that's how the mind works for every single human being who experiences it. Not everyone has experienced terror in such a radical way, so to them obsessive and compulsive behaviors seem very bizarre—but to the person experiencing such intense panic, it is important, gratifying, and seems lifesaving. As it relates to observing someone with an eating disorder, understanding the degree of survival driving his or her behavior would be very helpful in understanding what's going on and what to do.

For people suffering inside their eating disorder (or any addiction), the terror and perceived violence that presents itself is so intense that the destructive consequences of their coping mechanisms are acceptable in those moments. When the destruction and loss that occurs as a consequence eventually becomes bigger and more damaging than the apparent terror they're trying to escape, *choices present themselves.*

You can stop the abusive and damaging behavior, but the cost is facing the horror that seems like you can't survive. Or you can do what you already know relieves and hides you from that danger, but at the cost of continued suffering and damage to your life.

All of these fears stem from evolutionary wiring that presumes *you will die* without having whatever you've attached your security to.

Email requesting my help from 31-year-old female: I have been suffering from disordered eating for over a decade. I've lived with constant fear of being judged most of my life. To cope I turned to body image. Restrictive dieting evolved into

anorexia and orthorexia, and then full-blown food fears into exercise bulimia, and now binge eating. I have been in therapy but can't shake my disordered eating.

Body image is holding me back from living my life with confidence. I have overcome so much, including marriage to a drug addict, divorce, moved to Tel Aviv from New York. I've lived in constant survival mode. Since I've been bingeing, I've gained 25 pounds over the past year, but I don't want to go back to obsessing about food again. Instead I'm abusing food and using it as a crutch, which is hindering me from living fully. I'm pretty smart, and have tried to psychoanalyze and heal myself. While I've had breakthroughs and made great changes, I still find myself going on autopilot, and turning to food. I've watched all of your videos. I believe you have the capacity and ability to help me solve this bullshit once and for all. I'm so tired of it preventing me from stepping into my life completely.

Chapter 2

When Admitting Failure Feels Like Death

"Were it not for narcissistic pride, a mistake or negative feedback would be experienced only as regret and ascribed to human frailty and fallibility. Mistakes help one retain humility."

– Dr. David R. Hawkins, author, *Along the Path to Enlightenment*

The Choice Between Suffering or Death

There comes a point in every person's experience who's suffering with an eating disorder that he or she realizes they are failing—that she's lost control over her mind and now is a slave to whatever her survival mind commands. Because of the intensity that her mind demands, it seems as if she has no choice, no sense of authentic self, and that she's lost her grip on reality.

This inner awareness that she's lost control is a pivotal point for people who are suffering this way, because it's usually when he or she reaches out for help.

She probably can't hold a job, can't go to school, has quit activities that used to bring her joy, failed at being able to accomplish simple tasks, and struggled to function socially without bingeing, purging, or seeming bizarre. In addition, her body might have real pain and damage as a consequence. What she thought was beneficial and safe to start is now clearly seen as destructive, harmful, and out of control. Eventually, she can't hide her struggle, and it's obvious to loved ones that choices are being made that harm not only her body, but her future and freedom to live.

Even if the collapse of control is obvious to everyone on the outside, to the person suffering, there might still be too many benefits to stop herself, despite seeming weird to others. Nonetheless, when those benefits come at a dark cost, and the losses and failures are felt in such a way that there's been an accumulation of enough misery, pain, and grief—he or she has hit bottom. *There comes a point within one's self, where failure is impossible to deny.*

Up until that point, to his or her primitive brain, the only choice is to survive with those behaviors. When the person sees clearly that he has lost a handle on his own survival, it can feel as if life is permanently going to be this way—as if there is no escape, or alternative. This is especially true when you can't imagine life without the security of your eating-disordered behaviors. For me, this is when the idea of suicide seemed like the only relief possible. In the worst of my suffering, I would rather end my life than to let go of my eating-disordered behaviors, because I didn't know there was an alternative.

Although, when I actually faced killing myself and what that would be like, the truth in my heart was different. I didn't want to suffer any more, and I didn't want to die.

This is when I had nowhere else to go, but to admit I had tragically failed. However, the moment I was willing to look at that fact was when things changed. When the clients I work with open themselves up to that truth, they too get some clarity, and then a choice appears.

This is like the moment when a dictator directing a war realizes he or she is irrefutably losing the battle, and the cost of destruction is too big to deny. You can either continue to battle in pride and denial until you die, or you can submit to the truth, lay down your weapons, raise your hands, and wave your white flag in surrender. The choice is between continued suffering, or to go into the pain of letting go—and to let it go, means facing what feels like the dangerous terror of the unknown.

Sadly, many people take their eating disorder survival to the grave. They would rather risk dying from the damages of their eating disorder than to face the pain of loss, and to surrender the illusions of safety he or she gets from the dangerous behaviors. The terror they experience seems too great to submit to, and it is truly heartbreaking.

When the Alternative is Humility

When I think about humility, I see it as the opposite of pride and arrogance…as a meek and truthful awareness of your human frailty. Unfortunately, it is commonly assumed in cultures that promote narcissistic concepts of supremacy that humility is a bad thing.

Expectations are promoted that don't give grace for the truth of human capacity. If you show signs that you are struggling, are weak, or incapable, it's assumed you are an inferior person. This doesn't encourage truthfulness or acceptance of one's growth in a learning process. Humility to accept the inferior truth of oneself in relation to idealistic expectations, allows for people to not feel bad about themselves, or to be defined as flawed when they struggle on their path of development. On the other hand, without humility, expectations are unquestionable.

If you don't match the concept of what you're supposed to be, you are assumed to be a lesser human being, worthy of shame. Without humility, you are positioned to lie about the truth, and to repress the natural fragility of your human nature. You aren't allowed to be real, because being real isn't good enough if it isn't superior.

Based on concepts of supremacy, admitting failure is like quitting, and quitting is a sign of weakness. Weakness is a character flaw that is worthy of criticism, judgment, and exclusion. Weakness and failure are seen as a symbol of ineptitude and can be used to define someone as an inferior human being; someone who is less worthy of love and forgiveness. By believing this, you are setting yourself up to hide and repress any sign of weakness, inferiority, or loss of status. *You would be impelled to lie, deny, and place blame on the world around you.*

It would seem disadvantaged to admit you are struggling, are vulnerable, or have failed. Humility would open your mind to the truth, which includes the possibility of inadequacy and being seen as a failure.

When you believe narcissistic ideas of supremacy within yourself, you'll expect that of others. You'll feel you are worthy of abandonment, and that will spark the fear it might be true. If you fail, you'll assume you'll be shamed and scorned and as a result, fear will be triggered. The risk of exposure will bring about feelings of embarrassment if they looked down on you, made fun of, mocked, and discarded you from the community as a worthless loser. However, before experiencing those feelings, your survival mind will distract you with a solution that would relieve you of that risk.

When those vulnerable feelings trigger survival mechanisms that elicit sensations of psychological danger the same way it would in the presence of a predator, you're surely going to freeze, fight, or run and hide. The predator isn't an aggressive hungry bear; however, it's the danger connected to being exposed, rejected, and abandoned.

NOTE: *Eating disorders, and other forms of "addiction" function as a way to strengthen and control your sense of weakness and fear that in failure, you're a worthless human being.*

At some point, the idea that being fallible as worthy of shame and exclusion was internalized and believed to be true. Therefore...

- Being seen as weak, inferior, or incompetent would feel

threatening to a person's survival drive to feel worthy of love and inclusion.

- You will be impelled to promote arrogance, pride, and to inflate oneself to be stronger, better, and more superior than what the truth really is.

- In a narcissistic culture that characterizes weakness and inadequacy as "bad," it's beneficial to deny any failures, to repress your insecurity, and to instead deflect blame onto the vulnerabilities of the outside world as the problem.

This makes it seem as if the fear and judgment of weakness doesn't stem from within, but rather it is brought on by some "unfair" external force.

Therefore, when challenges arise instead of looking inward to develop a sense of understanding and competence, your inclination is to either judge and shame yourself as weak and pathetic, or to feel victimized by the difficulty. The connection between shame and binge eating has been studied for years.

> **IMPORTANT:** I go into great detail about this connection in the first section in the book *Diet Supremacy: The Toxic Bond Between Shame, Dieting, and Emotional Eating.*

The only solution would be to find an outside rescuer, shelter, or a controlling form of self-defense that will *give you an excuse, the appearance of strength, and keep you from being exposed as inadequate to handle challenges.*

In other words, the shaming of anything other than what's "superior," this positions people to hide or deny the truth of their humanness. They inflate themselves in pride to be bigger and better than they truthfully are, which requires a form of extreme commitment to constant proving of themselves. Or they shrink and hide who they are, in denial and afraid of finding out the truth. People are positioned to find a way to cope for the blame that is directed at themselves.

IMPORTANT: You can read more about this in chapter 3 of *Body Supremacy: Exploring the Torment of Eating Disorders as a Syndrome.*

You're either impelled to fix everything in that exact moment (purging or exercise bulimia), or you're doomed to hide until you feel capable of fixing things later (future dieting).

An example of this would be when they are seen in public, why people feel the need to excuse why they've gained body fat. People say things like, "I've had a hard time in life, so I took a break from dieting and plan to start up again soon." This person can't see that:

- ✓ She is using food as an emotional coping mechanism.

- ✓ For that reason, the diet restrictions she's promoting aren't actually realistic.

- ✓ The need to explain this to people is a way to deny the weight gain as not "real."

- ✓ Committing to others that she'll lose the weight later helps her avoid internal feelings of inadequacy, failure, and embarrassment. It also keeps her from feeling exposed, even though her body is factually exposed anyway. Saying she'll lose the weight is a form of denying the truth of her body.

✓ By promising she'll lose weight later, she is confirming the belief that more body fat is bad. She is sustaining ideas of thin supremacy.

What would happen in this example if the person were to admit how unrealistic dieting is for her? What would be different if the truth of her body fat without dieting was accepted without excuse?

• It would feel exposing, as if others would find out the truth that she's a failure at being thinner. She would be faced with questioning if she actually believes she is worth less if she has more body fat.

• Saying nothing when people can see the truth, allows others to think what they want. Having a story or an excuse gives this person the illusion she can control what others think, and it takes away the discomfort of having to face *the vulnerability of disapproval.* The cost is that she is now committed even more strictly to diet, starve, and restrict for those people. Therefore, she lives in isolation and misery, so that when those people see her again, she can prove her worth to them…for that one moment.

• If she were to say nothing, and others are giving the freedom to think what they want, even if they think in a demeaning way, the truth is exposed and the opportunity to move on presents itself. This would require enough reverence to accept the truth, and the humility to recognize you are not "bad," even when others don't agree. Once the truth is known, the servitude and bondage to proving otherwise goes away, and there's no pressure to continue to lie.

- This decreases the pressure for this person to diet as a "performance" to prove to others she isn't a failure.

- As a result, there's less pressure to strictly restrict food, decreasing the impulse to overeat, and this frees her mind to focus on the issues underlying her emotional eating. *Without having to defend yourself, you are free to be real and truthful about yourself as a human being.*

The power of humility is that it opens the door to the inner feeling of wanting to know the truth. It is what impels people to seek the vulnerability of understanding, rather than staying paralyzed in denial. People get stuck in their fear of the truth, because to their rigid supremacy mind, there is only one truth and that is winning, and winning is surviving. Without humility, the mind is closed to any alternative.

Lack of humility is why people stay committed to their arrogant state of pride, despite losing everything, hurting those they love, and causing destruction around them. In supremacy, they'd rather hurt themselves and others before they'd admit failure or accept a loss in status. If they fail, the only way they can remain positioned as superior is to make sure everyone around them fails too.

In the case of an eating disorder, without humility you are forever held to the idea that you are worthless unless you lose weight, eat healthy, or remain thinner when you achieve it. Therefore, you are permanently shackled to the behaviors that keep you in the solitary confinement of your mind. Without humility, you aren't allowed to fail, and you're not allowed relief from your eating disorder.

**Without humility, the eating disorder isn't a choice...
it's a demand.**

However, with just a small amount of humility, the narcissist is given the slightest wiggle room for grace. There is distance from the supremacy that allows her to look at things with compassion, and she is given clarity to see the truth. *There is no shame in failure, but rath*er, *shame exists in the expectation that failure isn't an option.*

Humility gives narcissistic standards lenience so that people held to them aren't defined as bad or worthless for failing or quitting them. In that state, the beliefs are separated from the essence of the human being, and the distance between the two allows for clarity and for reality to show itself.

You are given the space to look at beliefs about life, food, body image, and what a human being should be required to do in order to prove their worthiness. With that, you are positioned to question supremist ideas given to you about thinness and fatness, health and disease, and the idea that other's perception of your body being good or bad are valid.

The importance of humility is that it is the antidote to toxic pride that won't allow you to surrender, even when it is clear you have failed. It is what allows you to admit failure, without collapsing into a dark spiral of shame. Humility is what allows for forgiveness.

> *"The key to painless growth is humility, which amounts to merely dropping pridefulness and pretense and accepting fallibility as a normal human characteristic of self and others."*

– Dr. David R. Hawkins

Email from YouTube Follower in her 30s: *Hi Robin, I am thinking of scheduling a consult with you. I have been watching your videos for a while and have taken great inspiration from them. To give a bit of background, I am 150 pounds and have ranged from almost 300 pounds down to 115 pounds. I have had a gastric sleeve, reducing the size of my stomach, and after four years, with a little stomach stretching, and the stress of having a new baby, my problems have come back to me and old wounds have resurfaced.*

I am still suffering with post-partum depression and I had a bout of post-partum psychosis, which means I am on long-term antipsychotic medication. I have recently put on 28 pounds —and I have been told the medication I am on stimulates the appetite. I am at a loss with what to actually do with my appetite as I was used to having almost no appetite with the reduction of my stomach size, to now having quite a normal-high appetite.

I am on a lowered dose of ******** which has lowered my appetite a little but I struggle a lot to not feel guilty when I eat. I question whether my hunger is authentic, drug-based or a psychological craving. I was diagnosed with post-par-

tum Obsessive Compulsive Disorder, so I tend to over-analyze and question absolutely everything as I am basically a control freak.

I like to know that the future will be okay, but the more I fear food and try to control it, the more I binge on it. I notice I am pseudo dieting all the time, which feels like it's subconsciously running on in the back of my mind because I have body dissatisfaction. No matter what I tell myself about trusting myself or loving myself as I am, I still want to be slimmer or at least know I won't put on weight.

SECTION 2

Preparing to Let It All Go

My various individual journal entries from April 1997

"...I woke up feeling good but I'm nervous that I will want to binge because of the anxiety of being at my parents' home. I am going to the store and that makes me nervous. I'm scared that by being here, I won't be able to pay the rent for my apartment at school. I'm hungry now but I'm afraid to eat. I don't think I can wait another hour to eat with the family...It's 2:30; I just ate lunch and I'm too full. I HATE this feeling. It bothered me to see that Katie (my little sister) eats less food than I do, and she has no problems. I want to sleep."

"...I don't want to eat any more today...I wanted to binge after my snack today. I don't have much energy, but I'm wearing a pair of jeans I wore in high school and they are a bit baggier on me now. I hope I don't lose any more weight because I don't have much strength anymore."

"...Today was tough. My hardest day so far. I ate over 1500 calories in food. I am nervous to travel tomorrow and will try to keep myself busy. I scared that if I get bored I'm going to want to eat. Today I talked to Mom and Dad and I told them I am

having a lot of panic attacks since I've stopped puking. I am glad I'm getting better but I'm scared I'll get fat... That's the anorexia speaking."

"...Today was hard. After I ate dinner, I still felt hungry so I kept on eating. I knew I was going to throw up. When I was taking a shower, Katie was in the bathroom, and I decided to puke anyway. She got Mom and Dad and I had to sleep in their room so they'd know I wasn't puking... I feel bad because I lied and told them I was okay, when I actually wasn't. I wish I didn't feel fat when I ate. Dad told me to not trust my emotions or feelings because they are deceiving me. That is so hard to do, but I am going to try. I love my family so much and I want to make them happy and also to make myself happy."

"...Today I got in a fight with Dad. This made me so sad. Mom talked to me and said he was angry out of fear and because he loves me and wanted me to get better. My parents found out today that I smoked pot and that I'm far in debt. I bought a bunch of dieting books and clothes and sold my grandma's furniture to help pay for it all. My mom was so upset. I had anxiety about them finding out, and I could tell they were disappointed in me. I felt so fat that I decided to puke today. Hopefully tomorrow I will be able to work out. My muscles feel like rubber. I hope I didn't gain weight today."

Chapter 3

Compassion for Your Suffering

"*Compassion and love are not mere luxuries. As a source of both inner and outer peace, they are fundamental to the continued survival of our species.*"

– His Holiness the Dalai Lama

The truth is, when it comes to eating disorders that have resulted in obvious physical damage, restrictions in life, and the loss of relationships and opportunity—you have failed. You failed to manage everything your codependent relationships with those disordered behaviors required, and at the same time be able to grow and flourish in life.

Is that something to be ashamed of, especially when every ounce of your mind has been devoted to studying diets, nutrition, what you should and shouldn't eat? Should you be ashamed of failing, when you've been fanatical about weight loss, body checking, tracking points, calories, grams, and every microscopic aspect of food, exercise, and metabolism?

When you consider that every waking moment is defined by the shame you have about your body fat, the constant pressure to be thinner and to eat less, all while trying to repress the developing desire to binge—*did you not try enough*?

Ask Yourself:

- If success requires more devotion, more thinking about it, more perfection, more effort, more studying, more intense obsessiveness, and more from the little life source you have left, do you really want to succeed?

- If safety requires obsession, is it really safe?

- Should you be holding yourself to goals that are so radically out of reach that they require constant maintenance of perfection to succeed?

- Should you feel ashamed of yourself for struggling to manage survival when it demands you sacrifice your identity, your mind, your spirit, your life, and your body?

- Is failing at diet and thin supremacy, when it promotes mental illness, something to be ashamed of?

- Is eating "bad" food really worthy of shame?

With humility, you are given the space to admit failure—to admit that what you're doing isn't "healthy," and it isn't something you'd suggest to anyone. Your voice would be freed to express the truth about your suffering, and the detriment that narcissistic thin supremacy beliefs have had to your sense of self-worth. You can admit how horrendous are the consequences that diet supremacy beliefs have had on your relationship with food. You are given the space and separation to stop defending what has been a source of destruction in your life, and to give yourself grace and forgiveness from it all.

This reminds me of what I wrote in *Body Supremacy*, chapter 4, pages 83-84:

> *"A safe space with family and friends where a child can be truthful when she's vulnerable to criticism is fundamental to cultivate humility.* Humility allows a person to express the honesty of his integrity and expose the truth of his faults, without being defined as "bad." With this grace, children learn that being "special" doesn't mean you have to be perfect, the best, or better than others, in order to be accepted and worthy of love. It also means you don't have to strictly internalize cultural ideology that you don't naturally align with, in order to be worthy of love.

> "According to Dr. Kristin Neff, an author and psychologist from the University of Texas, self-esteem is an inner evaluation about how valuable a person is: very valuable, not so good, not valuable at all.[2] This is different than self-compassion, which isn't about self-evaluation at all, but rather about being kind to oneself. According to Dr. Neff,

'Self-compassion is a healthy source of self-worth because it's not contingent and it's unconditional. It's much more stable over time because it is not dependent on external markers of success such as grades.'

"A humble approach to mistakes and successes is essential when transcending narcissism to develop a sense of self-compassion that is true and real, and based on inherent competency. Ultimately, this teaches a person to hold inner grace for herself, and it allows her to be self-directed and realistic about her capacity, risks, and goals, even as others around her are more advanced. *A person with this type of self-awareness is less likely to internalize "specialness" as what makes her life important.* So, when she makes mistakes, is inadequate, or inferior when compared to others, her life doesn't lose meaning or value."

The importance of forgiving oneself from being held to merciless rigid beliefs is something I try to help every person I work with realize. They are so devoted to their controlling narcissistic belief systems that they live in shame and as indentured servants to exhaustive efforts required to make mistakes feel better and to prevent any more wrong. The more mistakes they make, the more "fixing" they have to do, and eventually their entire life is no longer free because they are "indentured servants" to making their wrongs right. To me, that is what hell feels like, and there is no escape until the survival attached to those beliefs are surrendered.

If the beliefs were inherently more loving, kind, and understanding of human nature, people would have the freedom to experience the complexity of life without fear of what's right or wrong. In terms of body image, if they didn't believe thin(ner) supremacy ideology to such a degree, they wouldn't...

- Be so fearful and ashamed about body fat,

- Hold themselves to such rigid dieting beliefs, and they wouldn't be suffering to such a horrific degree.

- Want to lose weight so intensely that they are willing to starve themselves—some people to the point that they trigger survival mechanisms to binge.

- Be so devoted to their body image that they're willing to hurt their body by vomiting up food, and even submitting themselves to (self-induced) cruel exercise routines.

Living in the torture of an eating disorder isn't an indication of lacking "willpower" or effort. It indicates the opposite.

If the goal is so high that it requires your entire life be devoted to losing weight, staying thin, and feeling ashamed if you don't—to the extent you have animalistic impulses to binge, do you really want to succeed?

For me, I chose to fail. I succeeded at reaching the goal, but with the unrelenting work and obsessiveness it took to reach and keep that goal, *I was literally living in hell.*

Where Does the Shame Exist?

When people see the radical effort and exhaustive obsession they've put into body image and dieting, which has only led to bingeing and other forms of self-harm, they realize that they shouldn't be ashamed for failing. It is the belief system that should be ashamed for teaching that it's "healthy" for people to live such inhumane lives in order to be accepted. *The shame resides in the graceless and merciless belief.*

Once a person sees that her devotion and effort is far beyond what anyone should be expected to do in order to "fit in," she realizes that her failure and inadequacy is worthy of compassion, understanding, and forgiveness. Given the context of the unrealistic and inhumane standards of the thin(ner) supremacy belief systems, she doesn't deserve to live in shame or be defined by the suffering she lived while supporting that culture.

Failing extremist expectations is commonplace, and more people need to speak out about why in a way that isn't shameful. Then people who are new and naive to thin and diet supremacy don't have to go through the same misery figuring that out.

When people want to be thinner, they don't know what it entails, especially when they're raised in a family and culture that self-righteously promotes dieting and thinness. People make the best decisions possible, based on what they are aware of under the context. Until they are aware of and experience the consequences, they can't make better or different decisions.

For me, it took the decision to commit suicide to finally look at everything with humility, to admit failure, and to see the ridiculousness of it all. And it wasn't until then that I had the courage to accept the truth, gave myself grace from the controls, and had compassion for how intensely I had suffered.

Compassion for Yourself and the Beliefs

I try to help people see that *everything is completely forgivable* when you give context to regretful decisions. For example:

- You were naive, impressionable, and did what you were taught and learned in order to survive. If you knew back then what you know today, you clearly wouldn't feel bad about your body, or make the same decisions. It took incredible pain and suffering to understand the downside of those choices.

- Even if what you were doing in your disorder was weird, wrong, and harmful to others, if it was the only way you knew how to escape feelings of horror and impending doom—as if you were going to die—it seems like you have no other choice. The only option you had was to reason, rationalize, and negotiate with your fear in order to repress the guilt.

- When you were in that state of mind, you didn't understand why your survival was so defined by what continued to bring harm to yourself and others. If you did know why, it wouldn't have been so difficult to stop.

- To shame yourself as if you did know, and you chose anyway, is ignorantly judgmental and cruel. However, that ignorance makes sense when you realize it's a survival defense mechanism, stemming from supremacy. When you expect yourself to be better than you actually are, as if you should know better, you're presenting a biased version of yourself that is the best-case scenario, *for narcissistic supremacy*. It's a stretch of your imagination based on what you wish you were, that seems will earn you love and inclusion.

- You can wish you didn't eat so much, but if you don't take into account how eating shelters you from anxiety and intense levels of fear, feeling guilty about it means you expect yourself to stop, without acknowledging the actual problem.

- Holding yourself to being better, when you don't quite understand how or what that takes, deserves understanding. Guilt-based "should" statements come from presenting yourself as stronger and better than you are, as a way to protect yourself from potential threat. When you realize the truth of your ability *is the truth*, no matter what you "should have known," you can forgive the inflated idea as a lie, in order to accept the truth as good enough. Whether you like it or not, *it is what it is.*

Thin(ner) supremacy and all other supremacy systems that preach dogmatic rules and controls, serve a purpose for people who have no other means to feel valued and that they "fit in." Despite the fact that they can be harmful and have limitations in freedom and independence, they serve a sense of safety for people, and are appropriate for those who need external controls to function.

The rigidity of controlling beliefs makes sense when you look at them as mechanisms stemming from survival mode. All-or-nothing thinking, catastrophizing, and fear-based beliefs that promote rigid controls would be what anyone would and should do if she truly believed her life was threatened. Because of this, controlling belief systems shouldn't be demonized, es-

pecially if they help and aid people who feel safer with themselves and others because of them.

Understanding that these systems serve an aspect of growth, learning, and evolution means it is every bit as important to be controlled and suffer, as it is to open yourself up to the pain of vulnerability and be set free. When there is compassion for all survival mechanisms, including narcissism and every aspect of our human nature, there is no reason to feel victimized by 1) your past, 2) others' attempts to control you, or the fact that 3) you had to suffer to such intense degrees to figure it all out.

The truth is, expecting to keep your body and food consumption in such a controlled condition is inhumane, abusive, and a form of torture. No human being on this planet deserves to live that way, let alone be praised for starving themselves.

> **NOTE:** For some people, the repeated attempt to restrict food has been with them for most of their life. It's not surprising to me when I work with people who've chronically been on and off diets that they have symptoms that look like a complex form of Post-Traumatic Stress Disorder (PTSD). This makes we wonder if binge eating is a symptom of "Diet PTSD."

> **IMPORTANT:** This content about "Diet PTSD" is described in more detail in the book *Diet Supremacy: The Toxic Bond Between Shame, Dieting, and Emotional Eating*, Chapter 5, An Experiment in Starvation, pages 69-78.

"Fear, rage, and pain, and the pangs of hunger are all primitive experiences which human beings share with the lower animals. These experiences are properly classed as among the most powerful that

determine the action of men and beasts. A knowledge of the conditions which attend these experiences, therefore is of general and fundamental importance in the interpretation of behavior."

– Dr. Walter B. Cannon, *Bodily Changes in Pain, Hunger, Fear, and Rage*

Chapter 4

The Courage to Surrender Your Survival

"All suffering comes from a person's inability to sit still and be alone."

— Anthony de Mello, author and spiritual teacher

> **IMPORTANT:** This chapter is more understandable after you've read:
>
> - Section 4 of *Thin Supremacy: Body Image and Our Cultural Battle with Weight,*
>
> - Section 3 of *Diet Supremacy: The Toxic Body Between Shame, Dieting, and Emotional Eating,* and
>
> - Section 4 of *Body Supremacy: Exploring the Torment of Eating Disorders as a Syndrome.*

The Safe Isolation of Your Eating Disorder

It's easy to justify continuing a destructive relationship with dieting, exercise or food, thinking that someday your life will be easier, you won't feel so insecure, and you'll eventually reach the goals you want in order to have the strength needed to live your life fully. For me, and for every person I've ever worked with who believed in cultural dogma like thin and healthy supremacy, that day never arrives. The more you need to keep yourself safe, the more your safety depends on the eating disorder behaviors, and the weaker you become to handle your fear. Eventually your dieting or bingeing safety mechanisms hold hostage your freedom to live, and it feels like you're trapped in solitary confinement.

When you get used to solitary confinement, studying the walls, cracks, corners, and every minor detail of that space brings you a sense of purpose, comfort, peace, and safety. It

also distracts you from the exit that leads to the overwhelming vulnerability of the outside world. This is what it's like studying diets, exercise, the content of food, images of others' and your own body.

The more you rely on the relief and comforts that your eating disorder behaviors bring, the more you remove yourself from what challenges you, and as a result the more fearful the vulnerability of life seems. As the outside world seems more and more foreign, and you feel weaker to handle it, the unknown seems scary. Fear of life without the safety that you know, turns into terror, and the comforts of your protection become more important. The controlling walls that keep you "safe" in confinement close in, and the space you live in gets smaller.

However, as the inside space of your life in eating disorder confinement gets smaller and smaller, eventually all that remains in sight is the comforting minutia of the sediment in the walls or the exit that leads to horror you assume exists on the outside. When facing that terror feels like certain death, suffering in isolation with an eating disorder can seem worth the misery.

✓ But as the walls close in…there comes a point when a person becomes clearly aware that if she continues, she'll lose further touch with reality—and

✓ Her mind will permanently collapse into psychosis.

✓ The physical damages will be permanent. Her body will die due to the hardship, and her life will be destroyed.

When your best and most forceful effort to survive deteriorates your life, you do one of two things: 1) Either you stay insane within the walls of your controlling survival mechanisms and die. 2) Or you *permanently* let it all go, abandon the only "safe" space you know, and step through the door into the terror of the unpredictable vulnerability of the unknown.

This means you are not only abandoning your dieting or bingeing safety mechanisms, but you are also willing to accept the truth of your body and expose yourself to a defenseless life with people, jobs, and family that you can't control. Ultimately, you are surrendering your survival to what feels like the potential of death.

The truth is, your eating-disorder coping mechanisms will eventually kill you, but with the eating disorder it seems as if you have control and can predict how you'll die. *This choice is a drawn-out, slower form of suicide.*

The alternative choice is that you could give up the safety of your predictable death, to instead face and accept the scary vulnerability and terror of an unpredictable death you aren't sure you can handle or control. The fact of the matter is, without the eating disorder, you don't know what would happen.

Because you've never allowed yourself to experience that fear without defense, you don't actually know the truth of what will happen.

Ask yourself:

- What would happen if in a state of surrender, you willfully refused to diet and allowed yourself to eat uninhibited, and do so without the belief you did something wrong, or that eating has ruined the day?

- What would happen if you sat through life's stresses without going to food, without seeking weight loss as the reward? What if the reward was to stop making food the main focus of your life?

Refusing to eat food as a way to escape life's stresses would be very different if there wasn't weight loss used as a reward. When the choice is made to willfully abandon the eating disorder in hopes recovery might exist, you are opening yourself up to the unknown.

> **It's important to see that is an assumption—not a fact—that you couldn't handle it.**

That assumption emanates from a sense of weakness or a lack of strength or capacity, but that is because you've never tried. You assume you can't handle it, and as a result you've always instinctively been guided by primitive survival mechanism that are wired to look away from vulnerability—not towards it. Also, you've always felt rewarded by turning away. To surrender your eating disordered behaviors would be like inviting your fear in—like facing what feels like the end of your survival.

The choice to do nothing when apparent danger exists goes against everything your brain, your survival, and your evolutionary psychology is instinctually demanding you to do. When it feels like you're going to die, doing nothing doesn't seem like a choice…but it is. The alternative is to face whatever it is you feel threatened by.

You could continue to suffer a slow, torturous, and inevitable loss of life in the predictability of the darkness and the certainty of your eating disorder survival. Or you could surrender it all, and do nothing, to instead face excruciating psychological pain as you willfully go into the uncertainty of your fear that threatens you will surely die. *One direction is what you know, the other is in the direction of the unknown.*

But when you clearly see you've failed one way or the other, and have the humility to admit defeat without shame, there is reason to surrender your eating-disordered behaviors. There might be a way to experience life in a different way that isn't as horrific, and that doesn't require you to lose weight first. There might be a life that isn't as bad, one you know nothing about yet. You'd have to open yourself up to what you don't know in order to find out.

> **MY EXPERIENCE**: *When I realized I wouldn't recover if I wasn't willing to accept permanent weight gain, it didn't make sense to feel sorry for myself. Being a "victim" of weight gain was a significant reason why I continued to suffer as intensely and as long as I did. If I wanted to recover, I had to take responsibility for the choices I needed to make. These choices were to:*
>
> 1) *Keep the misery and mental illness of the disorder to stay fit and thin,*
>
> 2) *End the misery by committing suicide, or*

3) *Accept permanent weight gain without complaint, in order to move on with my life without having to suffer.*

If I wanted relief, it wasn't a matter of being forced to face the possibility of weight gain and others rejection, but that I needed to willfully face and accept it. There was a feeling of want inside me that voluntarily surrendered the eating disorder behaviors in order to reveal the truth of my body, of other's disapproval, and to all of reality that needed to be exposed and accepted. It was pointless to feel sorry for myself as I knew that what had to be done would liberate me, and it was going to be scary…whether I did it sooner or later.

There was no risk in hiding from the truth of life any longer because the misery, torture, and insanity of the eating disorder was far worse

Humbly Accepting the Truth of Your Weakness

Without food restrictions, food morality and diet supremacy, puking food up or compensating with exercise, body checking and monitoring your size or weight, or bingeing, nothing will be there to protect you from what you fear the most. There won't be anything to shield you.

When it comes to real physical threats to life, you are *in fact* too slow to run away from a tiger, too weak to fight a bear, inadequate to live underwater, unable to fly, and are inferior to stop a train from plowing you over. Having that awareness of the truth is a good thing, and having tools and protections would be the right thing to do. When your sense of threat arises from a weak sense of strength to handle being criticized, seen as weak, or judged as someone who isn't as valuable, the only way to be relieved of the work and behaviors you've used to hide would be to face, accept, and forgive each and every one of those derogatory feelings.

Until it is clear to you that your fear stems from the assumption that *you can't handle feelings of loss, criticism, embarrassment, and rejection,* you will continue to rely on outside forces to survive. However, those outside forces are what you're seeking relief from—and why you suffer. If you are independently willing to humbly face, accept, and experience your inner sense of weakness as the truth of your capacity, no matter how pitiful and non-existent it feels, and if you're willing to accept being seen as worthless because of that weakness, *those threats lose their power.*

Therefore, in order for you to escape the controls of your eating disorder, it's inevitable you'll have to permanently surrender the symbolism of strength attached to your body image and eating, and all hope that you'll ever be thinner in order *to expose the weakness you feel within yourself.*

> **You will have to surrender all of the eating-disorder behavioral "weapons and shields" that seem to protect you from the underlying terror that's been so intimately a part of your life, but that you've been at war with.**

For me, this was like inviting myself to be killed. This is the complete opposite directive than what your body, emotions, and survival brain tells you

to do. The impulses stemming from the mind become so intense, and the body responds accordingly. Your hair will stand up on end, your skin will sweat, and your heart will feel like it is going to beat out of your chest.

Every cell in your body is going to scream for you to run and hide. It is at this point you could simply order a couple pizzas to eat, go puke up the food, get up and exercise, measure your weight or the size of your waist, or plan how little you'll eat the next day. It would be so easy to remove the incredible anguish, exposure, and the pain that feels like certain death. That's what you do so well.

But doing what you've always done, and now do so well, would mean you're going back into isolation—and choosing the comfort of your eating disorder's "solitary confinement." Choosing the comfort of immediate relief keeps you shackled to the behaviors that are the source of your misery, and you will eventually cycle around again to be confronted with the same exact pain and terror you've been too afraid of to face.

When an eating disorder is what has kept you safe and hidden from exposure, letting go of bingeing, dieting, exercising, purging, and checking your size and weight literally feels as if you're entering a space you've never been before. You don't know what to expect and have no bearings on if you can handle it or not. The risk of leaving the safety and predictability of a life you already know to then enter a new life you might be too weak to handle, and you have no clue about—feels like suicide for many people.

The willingness to accept the truth, even when it comes with excruciating psychological pain, is a powerful act of faith. This is especially true when there is no sense of what life will be like, or if you'll survive that pain. To me, this felt like I was jumping off a cliff that had clouds covering whatever was beneath the edge. I was either jumping to freefall to my death—or jumping onto something I didn't know existed.

Either way, I had to willfully leave the safety of the way I was existing and accept the risk that I could die, as well as the risk of the unknown.

Facing the exposure and terror without defense, even though you have no sense of strength to handle it, this takes an incredible amount of humility and courage. It isn't the courage to fight, but rather, the courage to do nothing, *with the sole purpose of finding out the truth* related to a life you know nothing about.

You will want to open your eyes and look at the terror—breathe it into your lungs, and invite it into every cell of your body. You want the truth. Warnings will enter your mind one after the other, suggesting you go back to the safe cage you had escaped.

These threats presume:

- You will be fat forever.

- You will have diseases, complications, and mobility limitations because of the body fat.

- You won't know what to do or how to live.

- People will make fun of you.

- They will find out you're a fraud.

- You will be pointed at, mocked, and made fun of.

- You will lose respect, and others will be seen as better than you.

- No one will be attracted to you.

- Your loved ones will reject you.

- You will be a nobody.

- You will be left to live life by yourself.

- You will be alone.

- You will die.

- There is no "you" that will exist.

Each threat represents fears you've been hiding from and thought you couldn't handle. Ultimately, if you don't want to hide anymore, and you want freedom from having to suffer with an eating disorder, you're going to need to accept every threat that arises.

As each threat arises, you compare it to the suffering and misery you've been living in. If you want recovery, you will want and willfully accept the threat rather than going back into the hell of your eating disorder. You will surrender to every threat in order to be free from the misery of your dark and predictable eating-disorder hell.

When Doing Nothing Does Everything

By accepting every threat and fear that arises, without defense, a person faces the potential end of her survival, which is the opposite of what our evolved mechanisms have wired us to do. This would be like standing in front of a tiger and doing nothing as it charges you, or accepting your fate, and peacefully walking to the guillotine. *Being nonresponsive to fear through acceptance is an act of courage.*

In essence, you are expressing a form of psychological strength, not by defending yourself, but by accepting the truth. This is a wisdom that requires, grace, faith, and courage, even if it means the ultimate risk of death. By doing nothing, you're accepting the truth of the outcome as good enough, and you use nothing but courage to handle it.

Every person I've worked with who has fully recovered willfully gave up his or her eating-disorder behaviors, and as a result, deliberately faced excruciating terror that felt terminal. With courage and faith, she chose the opposite of what her mind was telling her to do, and instead decided to be nonresponsive to the impulses to "do something."

What did she do?

- Doing nothing allowed her fear and terror to arise, and she chose to accept every threat that came up in order to get to the truth.

- She was willing to enter the vulnerability of a new life without having external regulation and protection from a rule book, a game plan, or dictator telling her what to do and how to be strong.

- In fact, she'd rather be judged and ridiculed because of her inadequacy than to suffer trying to prove strength that requires suffering. She graciously accepted her weakness in exchange for freedom.

MY EATING DISORDER EXPERIENCE: *Prior to recovering, I thought faith was believing that if you live the "right" way, the* *right thing will always happen. Faith is what you have when you want a specific result. You make certain sacrifices, and you do it in faith that you'll be blessed. I never thought that maybe the right thing was the opposite.*

With the old way of thinking about it, having faith meant going back to church in hopes my troubles would go away. Or if I stopped being so controlling with my diet, I had faith my fears of weight gain wouldn't come true. Faith came with the idea that with sacrifice there would be reward. I never would have imagined that faith would require I let go of the controls, and have the courage to accept the truth, which in my case meant accepting death.

When contemplating the idea of surrendering all of my eating-disorder behaviors, I remember thinking, "If this fear is going to kill me, maybe my denial and refusal to face it is going against what was meant for my life." I realized I was arguing with God or the truth of my life, by refusing to face the growing fear and terror that clearly wasn't going away. I thought,

> **"If the terror of death that is chasing me is God's will, then running away trying to avoid it is why I will forever live in misery and hell. If it's the truth of my life that am to die, then I will suffer in my unwillingness to accept it until I face that truth. If it is God's will that I die, then I have to accept that fact and allow it to happen if I am to be relieved of my slavery to what it takes, hiding in denial."**

These thoughts are what brought me to see that facing my fear of psychological death was the only alternative to facing a physical death by suicide.

I chose to face the terror of death I'd been avoiding, in order to accept the truth. And this meant everything from my previous way of life had to be mourned, reconciled, and released.

- I willfully stopped every coping mechanism that kept me safe.

- I stopped all forms of exercise, measuring food, judging and moralizing good vs. bad food, measuring my body and weight—and forced myself to face the truth of what would naturally become of my body.

- I permanently accepted that I might gain a few hundred pounds.

- I accepted the exposure that people would find out I wasn't the thin and fit person they thought I was, and they'd find out I was a fake and a failure.

- I refused to excuse or defend myself and then accepted the loss and embarrassment. If the truth is that I am factually an inferior and inadequate person, I accepted that too.

- I accepted that my family would think I wasn't good enough, meaning I might have to live on my own, or even be homeless.

- I accepted every threat that arose and every fear I had repressed so that I'd be free from having to hide any longer. Whatever the truth was, that's what I accepted, and ultimately, I had to accept death.

Once I surrendered and accepted it all, including my fear of death, I was able to leave the "solitary confinement" of my eating disorder to accept a new life I knew nothing about.

You can read more about my story in my book, *My Weight Loss Apocalypse.*

"We do not know where death awaits us: so let us wait for it everywhere. To practice death is to practice freedom. A man who has learned how to die has unlearned how to be a slave."

– Michel De Montaige, Philosopher from the French renaissance

SECTION 3

Living a New Life in the Same Body

Message from a client in her 40s who started dieting when she was 12—and suffered from anorexia, bulimia, orthorexia, and exercise obsession:

"How do I begin to explain how much you've changed my life? I lived my entire adult life with a raging eating disorder. It was so bad that I was bingeing and purging multiple times a day. When I wasn't purging, I was spending every waking second thinking about food, reading the latest diet books, or exercising obsessively. I did this all for one reason—so that I could stay thin. I believed being thinner would make me feel better, that health would improve my life, and that I'd be more confident in myself, my life, and in my marriage. Losing weight and being healthy became the purpose of my life. I have a master's degree in counseling, spent thousands on the "best" nutritionists and trainers in NYC, and have sought therapy and healing in all sorts of forms. I was petrified that I would never be healed, never live without an eating disorder, and never be "normal" around food. Nothing ever worked, and I was beginning to lose all hope.

"Losing weight and being healthy became the purpose of my life.

With your "no bullsh*t" guidance, I can honestly say that I no longer feel bad about my body. I no longer care to diet, obsess about food and exercise, care about whether I lose or gain weight, and I have not binged or purged in almost three years! I am healthier now than I have ever been—without dieting, obsessing, or trying to force my body to be what it's not. This healing has opened up my entire world.

"My mind is free to pursue things that interest me, I am confident in who I am, and my daughters have a role model they can actually look up to! You helped me to escape the confusion, shame, guilt and hatred I had my entire life, and now I live in freedom to be myself with grace, abundance and love. At first, it was NOT easy, but this process is life-giving and life-transforming."

Chapter 5

Inhabiting the Body
and the Life It Gives You

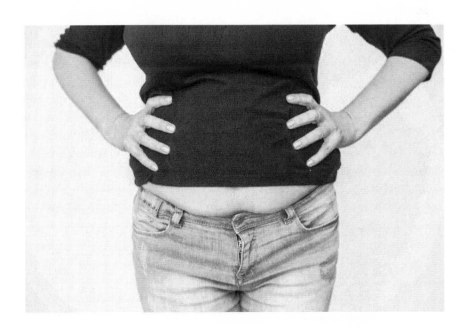

"The cessation of fear is the result of learning that the source of happiness is within. It stems from recognizing that this source is the joy of one's own existence, which is continuous and not dependent on externals."

– Dr. David R. Hawkins

Giving Up the Safety and Control of What You Know

Many people suffering with body-image obsession and disordered eating as coping mechanisms have never experienced a different way of thinking about life, and they can't imagine a different way to relate to their body and food. *They know only a life that believes thinner bodies are healthier, happier, more valuable, and free,* so in order to let the eating disorder go, they'd have to face the fear and accept the belief that they will forever be seen as unhealthy, inferior, and worthless.

When your survival brain and your experiences in life have reinforced that safety requires radical control, giving up control would seem dangerous and threatening—even when that controlled life was miserable, full of shame and hiding, and leads to suicidal tendencies. You're not likely to see that your suffering might factually stem from the idea that you can't handle life without being told the "right" way to do things. Whether you've been controlled by fear-based and controlling parents or teachers, an abusive boyfriend/husband, a totalitarian government or religion, or a narcissistic body-image culture like thin(ner) supremacy— if that's all you know, it seems as if that's the only way to exist. Leaving would feel dangerous.

> **MY EXPERIENCE:** *As I failed the rigid and unforgiving rules of the religion I was raised in, I compensated by gravitating to a similar narcissistic system of supremacy through body image. I reinforced thin(ner) supremacy the same way I previously reinforced the religion. My family wasn't hyper-focused on thinness and dieting, so when I turned to controlling my life with being ultra-thin and fit, it didn't necessarily come from my family itself.*
>
> *However, looking back, I can see that the totalitarian approach*

to religion conditioned me to seek a similar totalitarian system when I sought my own sense of survival. At the time, I could easily have been attractive to and manipulated by any grandiose narcissist, but because I was so traumatized by my "immoral" interactions with men, I gravitated to another controlling system rather than a controlling person. I clutched onto body image as if it was my new "special" religion, and my new means to feel lovable.

It's as if the culture of thin(ner) supremacy and the controlling nature of diet industry was a perfect replacement for the isolating fear-based system (religion) by which I was previously conditioned.

Instead of being a co-narcissist with a narcissistic religion, I became a compliant follower seeking approval from a grandiosely narcissistic body image and the diet and fitness industry.

To escape, 1) you will have let go of the safety in what you know, 2) experience the fear of danger and survival impulses demanding that you seek control, and 3) no matter how dangerous it may feel, you must refuse to respond without feeling sorry for yourself. To do this you'll have to accept the assumed danger and vulnerability that comes when you abandon an extrinsically controlled way of life in exchange for living a free life that is open and intrinsically self-directed.

This space comes with the scary truth that there are no rules and no one telling you who you are, what to do, how to do it, the way you have to be, or how to make right or wrong decisions. This space is massive and expansive with infinite possibilities, but it comes with the vulnerability of not knowing what to expect or having control.

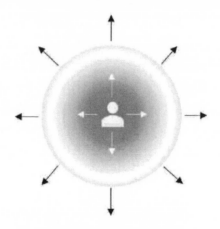

ACCEPTING THE UNKNOWN

*Intrinsically Self-Directed, Outward Focus,
Growth and Exploration, Expanding Life-Potential*

Grace and Forgiveness

Once people commit and open themselves up to a new life without dogmatic controls:

- They often ask how they'll know what to do or how to make decisions.

- Many people who blame themselves for failing will hesitate, and still hold shame about their past.

- They feel defined by their failure and losses, and fear they'll "ruin" life again.

- They feel that being "in control" gives them a sense of capacity to handle life.

However, being overly controlled has brought them a life of obsessive all-or-nothing thinking, anxiety, and worry, and is why they isolate themselves in shame and fear—it is *why they have suffered so greatly.*

> **If they want to recover from the controls that have destroyed their life, they must be willing to *give up the illusion that those rigid controls are safer.* To do this they have to question the rules and controls they have failed to follow that have defined the shame they feel inside.**

Are they truly the failure, or are the controls they held themselves to unrealistic, and do they fail to include the vulnerable laws of their human nature? Do their expectations have room for humility?

From my story written in *My Weight Loss Apocalypse.*

MY PERSONAL EXPERIENCE: I remember asking how I would navigate a new life without having a system giving me a sense of "control," and realized I needed to accept the vulnerable truth of my own capacity to make choices in life. I didn't want to repeat the same previous mistakes and live my next life seeking a different set of rules to constrict, confine, and control my life in exchange for approval and an artificial sense of strength and safety. By internalizing both religious dogma and social body-image dogma, I was lying to myself and the world about who I was, and about being "in control."

Ultimately, as I failed the religious rules and lost "control" over my life, these unforgiving rules and regulations were why I suffered with such intense amounts of shame. By letting the moral regulation go, I was able to speak for myself and recognize I was worthy of grace and forgiveness. Without the underlying shame, the need to compensate, control myself, and "repent" with a perfect body had lost purpose and meaning.

If I didn't believe or was hypervigilant to the religious "controls" that I believed kept me safe, I wouldn't have believed I was "bad" for what happened to me or that I was irreparably damaged. The belief that I had permanently destroyed my worth in the eyes of God for having sex, drinking alcohol, and smoking pot—and the resultant shame—was far more damaging to my psychological wellbeing and life than the actual sexual assault.

When I gave those religious controls grace, and I separated who I was from them, my entire sense of "me" changed. It went from being mentally constructed and controlled, to a sense of compassion and grace that had nothing to fear. In my new life I would live in the truth of what I was, even though there was no sense of control, or right-and-wrong rules to guide me.

Without the black-and-white way of thinking, I had clarity and distance to see that all of the choices I made in my past had been made with good intent and integrity. I did what people told me to do, because I believed their direction was more trustworthy than my own. Like all children, I did what I was told, and I didn't intend to ruin my life or anyone else's. If I were graded on intention and integrity, I would have been given an A, despite the fact that the outcome turned into an F. I obsessed over the "right" way to live, and held myself to such high standards that I ended up losing my mind.

I didn't fail because I lacked a desire to succeed, didn't want it enough, or didn't put in the effort. In fact, I wanted success so much that I completely devoted my identity and entire life striving to be good enough to adhere to rigid perfection. This led me to recognize that if my devotion and effort wasn't enough to succeed…I didn't want that success. I'd rather accept failure, be a loser, go to hell, and get labeled as inferior if it meant I was set free to just be me and be truthful about my authentic self and growth in my life.

Readers: What part of my life story resonates with you?

1. Were you raised in a controlling or fearful environment?

2. If not, were you attracted to friends or belief systems that were judgmental and controlling?

3. Have you experienced failures or losses that you internalized as permanently damaging to your worth?

4. Did that experience bring about shame and sense of worthlessness?

5. Are you trying to cope or feel better about it by controlling your body, access to food, dieting, exercising, alcoholism, drugs, or some other behavioral control?

6. If you could release yourself from being judged so harshly by those mistakes or experiences, would you need to cope the same way?

7. If you gave grace and forgiveness to the rules and controls you feel you failed, would you be able to see that you don't have to be defined as "bad" because of those mistakes or experiences?

8. How would giving grace and forgiveness to the beliefs, experiences, and to yourself change your life?

Letting Go of Needing Validation

Although the end result of thin(ner) supremacy and consequential eating disorder is a life lived in torture, panic, and isolation, what it's like to live that way makes *unconscious* sense only to the person who lives inside of it. Until she consciously understands what's going on, it is very difficult to escape the survival mechanisms that demands she clutch onto behaviors believed to keep her alive, while they're also impulsively urging her to hide, repress, and escape what seems to cause imminent death. Recognizing this is imperative in order for a person to have compassion and forgive herself, as these survival obsessions and compulsions might have caused irreparable damage to herself and others. Other people might never fully grasp the magnitude of the problem, unless they experience it themselves.

If it were possible to make a pill—which when taken would temporarily allow others to experience what it's like to suffer trying to survive inside the captivity of an eating disorder or *Body-Image Survival Syndrome*—it would be so much easier for people to understand why it seems impossible to escape. (I describe this idea of eating disorders as a syndrome in *Body Supremacy: Exploring the Torments of Eating Disorders as a Syndrome*.)

And if they knew the sacrifices and willingness it takes to recover, they would support whatever personal choices are necessary to start over, even if it includes being morbidly obese, leaving a family religion, ending a marriage, quitting a job, coming out as gay, or moving away to support her own life and dreams.

However, it is impossible to fully understand what it's like to suffer to such horrendous levels unless you've experienced it

yourself. For this reason, you are the only person who can fully grasp and provide the grace necessary as well as the mercy you need to be set free, even though important people around you might think you're wrong or that you have lost your mind.

A person who has suffered with binge eating might permanently quit all forms of dieting and will never try to lose weight again, even when she weighs over 400 pounds. To the naive, that seems crazy and unbelievable to accept. Because the freedom from the pressure to diet releases the survival impulse to binge, this decision can bring incredible relief and indescribable freedom to someone who's suffered her entire life with a binge-eating disorder. Only the person who is suffering knows what it will take for her to reach recovery, and although other people don't have a sense of strength and capacity to accept and handle those conditions, that doesn't mean she can't either. When it means ending a lifetime of suffering, she has a good reason to validate for herself why it's a good thing to let it all go and accept her body.

In order to surrender it all, you will need to substantiate *for yourself*—that what you've done and what you have failed at while seeking approval from others—is forgivable. You will need to validate for yourself that you don't need permission or approval before making decisions that are necessary in order to end indescribable psychological and physical pain and suffering.

> **MY RECOVERY EXPERIENCE:** *I know for me, if my loved ones knew the only other option for me was to commit suicide, they'd be rejoicing that I was willing to become obese, that I was eating "bad" food, or that I no longer defined myself by the shame that stemmed from the religious dogma. Instead of killing myself, I had to reverse decisions that I made to please other people while in my sick state of mind, decisions that didn't serve me or that were a source of my depression. I had to be willing to live across the country from my husband, in order to move back to the original university I'd left.*

This required that I was willing to face and accept the potential risk that our marriage might not be strong enough and would dissolve. I had to be willing to work and pay for my college education because I didn't have a scholarship anymore. After my "awakening" and full recovery, I had to validate for myself that these decisions were right for me, even though I knew I might be letting people down, or I might regret it later. I was willing to accept these risks as a better alternative to suicide.

You can read my story in *My Weight Loss Apocalypse.*

By validating yourself, you're setting others free from having to supply your needs, and you're releasing them from having power over your decisions. You are taking responsibility to acknowledge, assess, and to fulfill your emotional needs, which in turns allows you to relate unconditionally to others. If others are critical, you are free from having to internalize their opinions or defend yourself in order to instead, listen and understand. You become aware others have no idea what you've lived through or what is truthfully right for your life, therefore their opinion about your life can be understood without you having to do something about it. Of course, as children our lives depend on following our parent's guidance, but as we grow up and mature, there comes a time we must rely on our own inner sense of direction in order to guide the life we are living.

Message from 48-year-old woman who started dieting when she was 13 years old.

"I've gained and lost more than 100 pounds many times over the past 30 years. Even at my lowest at 145 pounds, I still felt it wasn't good enough. To be honest, my mind was at its worst when I was that lean. I was constantly posting pictures of myself

in a bikini seeking validation. I was admired and given attention and it felt good, but what people didn't know is that I was so paranoid about gaining weight that I was obsessively exercising and frantically trying to repress my urges to eat. All I thought about was my body, food, and how I could lose a couple more pounds. I joined every weight-loss group and shared my before-and-after pictures looking for praise, but all that did was add to my problems.

"I started bingeing again and the exercise wasn't enough to keep from gaining weight. I am a very driven woman. If I want something bad enough, I do whatever it takes. Each time I'd start my day eating perfectly, I'd end up bingeing. I'm now over 220 pounds, and I can't continue this way. The thought of losing weight again seems daunting, and I don't have it in me anymore. My thoughts are around how I feel, thighs rubbing together when I walk, tummy protruding out of my pants' top, and the not-so-fun symptoms associated with extra weight. I've been down this road so many times that I can see there's only one way I can get out of this—accept this body.

"I have to say one thing. I love me. I am the same person I was at 275 pounds as I am at whatever I weigh now, or what I weighed at my lowest. The only difference now is that I'm okay with my failure. I don't want to be thin again if it means I have to go back to that self-absorbed and fearful place. I can handle this body. I AM NOT BROKEN. Yes, I do want to be smaller and alleviate my symptoms, but I'd rather be like this forever if I don't have to spend one more SECOND feeling guilty about what I ate, or trying to figure out what foods I should avoid because it may be causing my issues."

Telling the Truth and Accepting Rejection

Even if your feelings are misguided, immature, and wrong, by using your truth to direct your decisions, you are taking ownership of your life and responsibility for the consequences. Taking ownership of directing your life allows others to experience who you truthfully are, and as you meet new people, those who are attracted to you are interested in the real authentic aspects of you that you share. Those who want a conformed and controlled individual, will judge the truth of you, and will naturally dismiss you as unworthy of their attention.

I've had many clients who believed they couldn't date or have loving relationships unless they were thinner. When you accept the truth of your body, you are accepting rejection. There are people who will not want to be with you or get to know you unless you meet a visible "standard" they feel safe with. It is a fact that when dating and seeking a mate, you will reject people based on their looks, and others will reject you too.

You're too tall, too fat, not fat enough, too hairy, too loud, don't have enough hair, don't have the right education, politics or religion, etc. By accepting rejection ahead of time, you are giving yourself the space and freedom to be who you are in truth, which includes having a body that is the way it is.

> **When you get to know the truth about yourself, and allow that to be what you present and express to the world, you will repel those who will judge, and you will attract those who truthfully appreciate your truth.**

It's much easier to comply to systems and "fit in" because it gives you a sense that you can control how you're accepted, *which is true*. In compliance, recognize you are presenting a façade that provides a small buffer between the culture you live in "the real you" that exists from the heart. When you live expressed from the truth of your heart, unrealistic and rigid societal standards that are presented as necessary in order to be accepted will lose credibility and become unattractive. This doesn't mean you don't want to dress the part or blend in with your culture, *which is human nature*. It means you aren't willing to diminish and shrink your true self and suffer, living a lie for someone else's ignorance and pleasure.

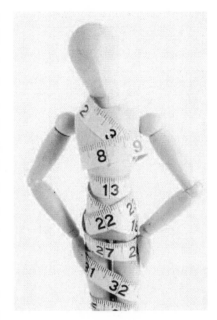

When you validate yourself from the source of your truth, it becomes pointless to work so hard for other's validation. You'll be able to discern people that want you to need validation, and you'll reject that relationship before it starts. The same goes for discerning cultural ideals, like narcissistic concepts of thin and diet supremacy.

When a person recognizes how unreachable certain body images are for her body, she is more likely to release herself from the totalitarian approach to it. She might still assimilate, but she won't so unforgivingly hold herself to it. It wouldn't define how she identifies her worth or the worth of her body. In the case of thin(ner) supremacy, she would be more accepting of her natural body, and less likely to hold herself to an image that would require unrealistic food restrictions, or diet supremacy beliefs.

To people who radically believe that thinner bodies are healthier, fitter, and more attractive, a person who accepts her natural body would seem crazy, stupid, lazy, or inferior. They don't understand how "body neutrality" could be acceptable when their supremist mind believes being thinner is always better.

For the rest of your life, it is inevitable you will be criticized and judged for not looking, being, or acting a certain way, and those judging people are clueless to how those beliefs might be completely inappropriate, unrealistic, and could negatively impact your life. What they are doing is projecting onto you the controls and conditions they need and can handle, as if your life is identical to theirs. They are projecting their survival needs onto you, and their suffering is worthy of compassion.

Accepting and Inhabiting Your Body

When it comes to the body, at some point you will have to accept it. It was born with mechanisms and DNA and genetics that are beyond human comprehension. Your body is vulnerable to all forms of pain, rejection, illness, deformation, limitations, and infinite ways to die. However, it is also capable of providing life, consciousness, and mechanisms that allow awareness, the experience of love, joy, loss, and the miracle of life in abundance that surrounds you. You have a choice:

1. Either you can believe the body isn't good enough yet, and point your focus towards fixing and repairing it, hiding it, and protecting it from vulnerability, before you inhabit it.

2. Or you can accept the body for what it is as good enough, including all of its vulnerabilities and inevitable death. You allow the consciousness the body is giving you, in order to focus outward toward life with all of its freedom and potential for you to experience.

Until you are willing to accept your body and the fact that it is vulnerable to pain, age, loss, accidents, and ultimately, death—you won't inhabit it. Without inhabiting your body, your mind will be closed to openly explore, enjoy, and appreciate life.

If you are attached to a body, and that body is supplying a consciousness you're aware of, you can accept it and occupy that life, or you can reject it, and instead occupy nothing while fixating on what has to happen until you're satisfied.

There are many reasons a person would reject her body. Physical or sexual trauma are common reasons. However, for many people the reason isn't as severe. She rejects her body because it poses a threat to her ability to "fit in." Her body is different than what is socially admired, and as her body is rejected by others, she rejects it too. Until she accepts her physical differences, her life will be fixated on ways to fix her body. Instead of resenting the body image she's trying to enforce, she resents her true body as if it's done something wrong.

In order to release your life from being trapped by the work it takes to change your body, you'll need to reject the body image and accept the truth of the body and its genetics as it is. Once that is done, the life that body is giving you can be experienced. However, you'll have to occupy that life as well as the reality that overbearing people will think you're living your life wrong too.

Reclaiming Occupancy of Your Life

As you forgive and surrender the old way of being in life, you open yourself up to a life that isn't centrally focused on controlling everything—or focused on having shame for not being able to control yourself. As it concerns body image, you'll be facing a life that isn't defined by your body, opinions about it, overeating, or restricting food. This can feel like a complete loss of identity, but letting that life go can free your mind and energy from going inward in self-preservation toward self-control, to expanding outward toward an open space of infinite possibilities and life potential.

MY RECOVERY EXPERIENCE: *I remember getting to this point and thinking it might be easier to just turn around and go back to* *the predictable life I knew, even though it was tortured, insane, and I was in the deepest, darkest depths of hell. As I pondered which would be worse, I realized that a new life would be better. Even if there's risk that a new life could be bad, there's possibility that it might not be as bad as what I was escaping. In that case, anything less bad would be better. This was when the fear and scary feelings that had risen went away as I faced freedom ahead of me.*

Anything, to include death, would be better than the existence I was escaping. There was no reason to fear the vulnerability of a new life and getting to know the true "me."

How can other people know what's right and wrong for you, when they don't occupy your life? Others might know what is right for the life they are experiencing, but how can they know what's right for your life if they aren't in your inner space of awareness to experience it? Only you have access to the inner-life space that is experienced by you, so it would be impossible for others to know what your needs are and what brings you joy. Not even your mom, dad, spouse, or closest friends have inner awareness of what you're experiencing. Only you know what, when, and how much, as well as the depth and degree of your needs.

To set "your will" free, you would need to honor the inner space of life that you are experiencing, take hold of it, fulfill your own needs from within, and independently use the life you're experiencing with the inner integrity only you can feel inside.

With this, you wouldn't have to convince ignorant people that you are worthy of life and capable of living in freedom, especially if you've already given yourself mercy and grace to figure it out ahead of time.

MY RECOVERY EXPERIENCE: Before my recovery, I needed other people to give me permission to live, and I changed everything about myself to become what others wanted. I molded my entire identity around another's opinions, and did what that person thought I should do, hoping that person would fulfill my need for approval.

After recovery, I choose to be truthful about myself and approve of myself, even if I was disapproved of, in order to live my life for me. Rather than give my life away and have someone else tell me what to do with it, I had to take ownership my life and trust I was worthy of doing it "my" way, even though I didn't know what "my" way was.

I had to trust my own sense of integrity to guide me and use my freewill to lead my decisions in life. I didn't know very much, but what I did know is that I didn't mean harm to anyone or anything, I had good and loving intentions, and moving forward I needed to use my personal integrity to make decisions. This was one of my most important realizations as I reconciled my past in order to give myself grace as I lead into my new life.

If I used my own personal integrity to direct how I navigated my life, I was doing the best I could with what I was aware of. It became obvious to me that I wasn't aware yet of what I didn't know. This meant that life could be directed only by the best of my integrity, even if I chose to conform to rules, beliefs, and regulations. The guidelines from my past were all the awareness I had. Therefore, it was impossible for me to know the risks and harms, until I fully went through it. I had to suffer so that I could learn and expand. I realized that's the only possible way to live. You do the best you can with what you know and are aware of, and until you know and are aware of something different, it's impossible be or live any different.

To hold myself to some expectation that requires I have a wider and much broader awareness would mean I'd be setting myself up for failure again. It would take trial and error for my awareness to expand, so moving forward I gave myself grace to live in that truth, even if it was factually inadequate or inferior to what others expect of me. I remember thinking, "If the truth is that I'm not good enough, I will no longer feel bad about it. If I'm a lesser and weaker human being, that is the truth no matter what anyone thinks about it. It has to be accepted by me, for me to work with it. I will work with what I have and grow from there. I'd rather be free and live within that framework, than try to deny it and be a prisoner to proving otherwise."

Readers: What part of my life story resonates with you?

1. Have you changed yourself to be more like someone else, hoping that person would like you?

2. Have you given up or rejected truths about yourself, in fear someone important might judge and reject you?

3. If you were to accept the truths about who you are, and were to accept yourself as "good enough," even if you aren't "good enough" to others, would you still change yourself for their approval?

4. Have you lost touch with "who you are" and what makes you "you" because you've adapted yourself to others' expectations, beliefs, and needs to gain their approval?

5. Even when decisions were made that you regret, did you truthfully know any different then? If you knew better, would you have done better?

6. What if you aren't the smartest, prettiest, or the best in any way? Could you accept this truth?

7. If it means freedom to be real and truthful about who you are, would you accept rejection and disapproval?

Giving Yourself Grace Ahead of Time

When you accept the truth of your nature and choose to work with it, no amount of criticism, rejection, and abandonment will matter because your competence, adaptability, and self-determination is based on what's realistic. In this case, most people would rather be alone and wait for the right people who love and accept their natural truth and the vulnerabilities of who and what they are.

People who want you to conform to them would rather you abandon your truth, sacrifice your happiness, to devote your life to doing and being what they want—for their happiness.

Giving yourself grace ahead of time—knowing that your awareness and integrity is the only truthful aspect about you that you need—will allow you to let go of control, and accept the vulnerability of the unknown. You are setting yourself free to independently exist in a space of freedom and infinite potential, and in that moment, you are no longer holding yourself hostage to any belief system to define and protect you and to fulfill your sense of worth and lovability.

As a person lets go of the body image to reconcile the losses of her eating disorder, and forgives herself for what she wishes she would have known, she realizes it's pointless to feel bad or have toxic guilt for what has happened. The best she can do is to recognize she knows better now, and from there she can do better. If she can forgive her previous ignorance, and accept her current naivety moving forward, she is more likely to accept and move toward the vulnerability of the unknown.

Giving herself the grace to be who she really is, allows her to start over, to live directed from the heart, rather than living from a past mindset that has only brought pain and misery to her life. With this she can permanently escape the culture of body image and resultant eating disorders, and she can recover independence and freedom in her life.

> **IMPORTANT:** I would recommend reading:
>
> - Chapter 10 from the book *Thin Supremacy: Body Image and our Cultural Battle with Weight,*
>
> - Chapter 10, 11, and 12 from the book *Diet Supremacy: The Toxic Body Between Shame, Dieting, and Emotional Eating, and*
>
> - Chapter 11 from the book *Body Supremacy: Exploring the Torment of Eating Disorders as a Syndrome.*

Believing within yourself that you have the capacity to thrive alone, and are innately worthy of being accepted, needed, appreciated, and wanted, *even when others don't agree*, allows the brain to relax its guard from survival mode. This allows you to experience sensations of safety, security, and a sense of completion *that all is well*. This is the unknown space of "recovery."

Chapter 6

Recovery and the Expanse of Freedom

"The realization that there is a source of joy and happiness that is beyond the ego is a major step. Then curiosity and an interest in how to reach spiritual goals arises."

– Dr. David R. Hawkins

Recovering Your Independence

After the old way of existing is left behind, even though you have no sense of what will come to be, a new existence presents itself. It is free, open, and hard for many people to describe. I know for me, once I made it out of my past life, and I was still alive—the freedom from such darkness is so magnificent, loving, gracious, and merciful that I've never returned. It would take a total regression or a loss of awareness for me to go back to that old way of existing, gripping tightly to prove myself with every ounce of my life.

Getting to the point where I had suffered enough that I was willing to die was the hardest part of reaching recovery. Letting it go, being weak, having humility, facing and accepting the truth, and starting over…that's the easy part. It is literally effortless.

As a result of letting go:

- ✓ The mind is released from the restrictions and demands of survival mode, leaving vast room for the mind to operate without having to be closed in, defensive or self-centered towards self-preservation.

- ✓ The brain is less sensitive to criticism, isn't afraid of mistakes or failure, is more adaptable to challenge, and the survival demand for perfection melts away.

- ✓ This allows experience to be felt from a gracious and relaxed state that is open, malleable, and lenient. Humility is always there.

- ✓ Without fear and rigidity, there is freedom of creativity, exploration, spontaneity, and innovation.

Maslow's Pinnacle Hierarchies of Need

(Continued from the first section of *Body Supremacy: Exploring the Torment of Eating Disorders as a Syndrome,* Chapter 2, pages 30-43.)

At a time and place where food is overflowing and abundant, with no end in sight, and our access to shelter and environmental safety is secured, it seems the main uncertainties of our modern society are directly related to threats to social-survival needs. In general, *most of the fears that people have and struggle to accept are threats of being judged, exposed as inferior, rejected, and permanently being abandoned.* I believe these fears stem directly from a person's unfulfilled and vulnerable third hierarchy of survival needs.

Because we are born completely dependent on others in order to live, its understandable why we would internalize what our parents, family, and friends believe, as if our comradery and loyalty to their way of living is vital to our survival. However, if your sense of lovability and belonging is based on "fitting in" or meeting demands that conflict with your true natural self, the conditions you must comply to in order to "belong" can be why you're triggered into survival mode.

Those extrinsic conditions are why you suffer, living a life that harms you so that other people's needs get met, in hopes that they validate your worth because you're deathly afraid of their rejection and abandonment. You have to prove your worth by meeting their standards, as if they control the security of your third hierarchy of need: social survival.

When you have to prove you're worthy of love and acceptance by achieving a body image that requires degrees of food deprivation and starvation, food is made to seem as less important than is other people's approval. *According to what required for sustaining life, this is backwards.*

93

As the third hierarchy of need "to belong" endangers the first hierarchy of need for food, a person's primitive survival mechanisms go through vicious cycles of back-and-forth conflict between controlling food restrictions and limitless food consumption. Food fulfills her innate sense of life security, but it threatens the thinner body image that seems to secure her social-survival needs. She restricts food to make her body more socially accepted, yet this triggers mechanisms that increase the psychological need for food. Her survival goes through an all-or-nothing pendulum swing that rises as she more desperately wants to lose weight, which intensifies the threat to her access to food, and this increases her urges and desires to eat. This is like endlessly chasing your tail or pursuing the benefits of a mirage.

When she eventually suffers enough and is ready to end the survival tension between her body image and her need for food, the only way she can end this cycle is to face the truth of her body and to accept her fears of being inadequate, worthless, and alone.

The fact of the matter is that her need for approval isn't required—but without food she will die.

By willfully sacrificing her approval and worth that has been attached to a body image, she is released from having to restrict or diet anymore, which ultimately relaxes the tension and survival mechanisms magnifying her impulsive need for food. Not only is her first hierarchy of need now safe and secure, but her third hierarchy of need is set free from depending on others to fulfill it.

I believe that by surrendering external conditions that provide apparent security to a person's third hierarchy of need, she is ultimately facing and accepting rejection. It is at this point she validates her responsibility and independently answers the questions of whether she is worthy of love and worthy of the life the body provides her.

By believing she is innately worthy of love and belonging, even when she doesn't meet the expectations and needs of other people, she fulfills her third hierarchy of need.

As part of my recovery, I remember wondering how I'd survive if everyone important to me abandoned me on the streets. I recognized that even if I was left to myself in the wilderness, as long as I had a way to get food and water, a tent with blankets, and some tools to make a fire, I'd be just fine. No one could take away my ability to work, create, or to learn. My will to work and figure things out was all the freedom I needed to succeed. *Having a sense of competence empowered me to see that if I could accept myself as unconditionally good enough, my life would be set free.*

The courage it takes to independently accept one's true self is the foundation of self-confidence, which opens the mind to curious wonderment, creativity, innovation, and exploration. Because the pressure to perform, please others, and to succeed at all cost is gone, the truth of one's capacity can be discovered and flourish. There is no need to control the outcomes of life, which means there is more willingness to take risks. It is at this point that a person transcends the crippling forces of survival mode to experience a different way the mind works.

––––––––––––––––––––

MESSAGE FROM A CLIENT:
"To me, Robin was like the angel standing in the middle of hell, showing me where the door to get out was. She educated me on Maslow's hierarchy of needs, narcissism, codependency and boundaries, where unhealthy ideas about food come from, and so many concepts. By the time I reached out for Robin's help, it wasn't hard for me to turn my life around because I really had nowhere else to turn.

"For the first time, I learned how to give myself grace, and what compassion actually feels like. I'll never forget when, in the ashes

*of my life, I first found that eternal smile that lives in the heart—
this eternal presence of a creative force that lives inside of each of
us. I imagine it's the place prisoners of war find when their spirit
cannot be affected by the external treatment they are receiving. I
also realized that I had compassion and grace I could give to others.
I found my heart and what it means to live from it. And I divorced
all concepts of dieting and restricting, and especially of seeing myself
as a failure.*

"*In the past, I had tried every diet in the book, in an attempt to
"control" myself. I hardly ever even think about food now because
I am too busy living life. Through Robin's contributions to the
world, I do believe my life was saved. It seems so radical compared
to the diet industry's rhetoric, but I truly understand that the mental prison of the restrictions we place on ourselves is far, far worse
than eating some food considered "forbidden." What came after
what had felt like I was facing death was true life and freedom. I
walked away from that mental prison, and I sincerely hope each
and every person struggling finds his or her own way out. The fact
that Robin didn't just 'free herself', but turned around to free as
many other people as she can reach, is a testament to how beautiful
and powerful her work is.*"

Maslow's Fourth Hierarchy of Needs: *Self-Esteem*

At this level of human expansion, risks are taken with an open mind. Time
is less restrictive, and is more relaxed and laid back.

The survival mode need for success through perfectionism diminishes;
therefore, there is less controlling-ness, and creativity is given the room of

objectivity, rather than forced through survival subjectivity. Experiments can be done without the all-or-nothing pressure of life and death. This is where many scientists, explorers, and self-determined navigators of life exist.

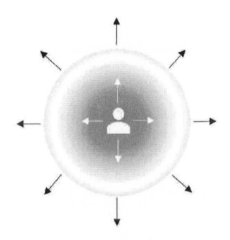

ACCEPTING THE UNKNOWN

*Intrinsically Self-Directed, Outward Focus,
Growth and Exploration, Expanding Life-Potential*

At this level there is less addiction, less depression, and more energized excitement with life that isn't so dependent on defending oneself, defending safety, or defending one's physiological needs. I remember the excitement I felt to explore my life after recovering from an eating disorder. I was willing to travel and to start a business, and I knew that no matter what, that my capacity to work, to create, to change, and to adapt to anything gave me infinite potential to create with my life. This was the case, no matter what limitations and loss came my way. I knew, not only could I adapt, but I could recreate a new life from there.

With the strain of survival mode removed, it would make sense that there would be a dramatic shift on how people feel physically.

Maslow's Fifth Hierarchy of Needs: *Spiritual Actualization*

The pinnacle hierarchy of need described by Dr. Abraham Maslow is called Spiritual Actualization. This level goes beyond self-esteem, expanding the mind, and exploring, to accepting life through the contentment of the spirit. The transition from self-esteem into self-actualization is described perfectly by world-renowned scientist, psychologist, and spiritual guru, Dr. David R. Hawkins (1927–2012). In his book *I: Reality and Subjectivity* he writes about exploration being innate to human nature, and at our highest level we ponder spirituality. He says,

> *"Exploration is innate to mankind, and at its highest levels lead to spiritual inquiry. This brings up the question of who am I, what am I, where did I come from, what is the origin and destiny of the self, and who and where is God."*

Once there is freedom to exist and explore, the next rise is to be present and allow life to ebb and flow without having to think, control, or manage any

of it. This requires total acceptance of death, so that fearful thoughts and the need to control the environment can be let go.

Self-actualization has often been described as the pursuit and realization of the spirit. To some this would also be described as enlightenment, or a higher state of consciousness. This level is also described as bliss, and is based on the freedom of the mind to witness, observe and just "be" without having to figure it out.

Message from 34-year-old client suffering with Exercise Bulimia: "Living life is starting to seem really fun. It's looks and feels like my own playground. I found myself pondering things like, "What wonderful things am I going to see and do today? Who will I get to talk to? Maybe I'll take a nap!" I haven't felt so open to life since I was young child! I can't believe I can do anything I want, and I don't have to feel the anxiety of being the best, doing more, or having to exhaust myself in order to earn dinner tonight. It's amazing and invigorating. It feels like pure happiness and I'm really enjoying it!

"It's weird now that I'm present and open to life as it is, I've noticed that I forget certain little things that I was doing before, and I don't feel the same sense of urgency or pressure to exercise. I can't believe I didn't even know I was suffering. I thought I was living the 'right' way. I want to really soak in and enjoy every moment.

"I'm starting to really see through a lot of societies' bullshit, and it's weird how I can watch television and see so many people trying to fill that void in their heart and sense of worth. With my new freedom, it's blowing my mind how many people I can recognize trying to feel better about themselves with outside validation.

"I'm in a happy and 'floaty' place, where experiencing life is all there is. It almost feels as if I'm in a fantasy world, living from my heart, and liberated from having to be so self-centered to prove myself. Every day I used to try to accumulate enough work and effort just to feel as if I wasn't a failure. There was no joy. Now I can simply be with life, and there's no negativity in my head nagging me to do something. Do something! DO SOMETHING! That has dis-

appeared. I feel like there's no boundaries, no guilt, and no stress. This is amazing."

———————————————

At the pinnacle of the hierarchy of needs, the concept of "me" separate from "you" disappears as context and relativity becomes obvious. Because of this everything is seen as forgivable. There is no "one" way to live, but "all" ways to live. All existence is born out of an expression of potential, inherent to life.

Enlightenment has been described as loving, accepting, and merciful. At self-actualization a person can relax her mind and allow life's energy to exist as it is, unconditionally, accepting death and all that life allows. There is no need to be right, or to make others wrong. This space is gracious, accepting, and is described as holy. To some who've experienced varying levels of self-actualization, it is heaven.

Indescribable Freedom and the Higher States of Consciousness [3]

(Continued from the first section of *Body Supremacy: Exploring the Torment of Eating Disorders as a Syndrome,* Chapter 3, pages 44-57.)

One of the most curious outcomes of recovery is the indescribably freedom, brilliance, and sense of lovingness that emanates on the other side of the darkness you just escaped. When you're willfully trapped in the darkness, leaving seems like the most horrendous nightmare that could ever exist. When a person chooses to leave the safety of that darkness, she has no idea what's on the outside of that space, making recovery that much more difficult. I know for me—I was willing to commit suicide before I was willing to surrender my eating disorder and face the fear of the unknown.

Time and time again, when a person I'm working with is willing to sacrifice her safety, controls, pride, and what feels like the end of her entire identity and life to enter into a new way of existing, she predictably experiences what I experienced too. It feels like a radiating openness that is weightless, and brilliant. Coming from a state of survival mode, there's no possible way a person can predict or fathom this way of existing.

Survival mode is self-centered, narcissistic, defensive, fearful, paranoid, controlling, forceful, rigid, and unforgiving.

Death is all or nothing so it would make sense that the cognitive distortions coming from that state of mind would be too. If all you've experienced in life is the fear-based forcefulness of survival mode, it's impossible to pre-conceive what you're going to enter before you go into it. You don't just imagine what recovery is, and then set goals to accomplish it. That is not how it works. The willingness to admit failure and to blindly surrender everything you know, without any guarantees of survival, has to happen first. You have to leave the safety of your "addiction," knowing that you could die without it. Once that happens, then the other side reveals itself. According to renowned psychiatrist, researcher, author, and spiritual guru, Dr. David R. Hawkins, in order to transcend the lower survival states of consciousness, all pride must be surrendered to reveal the truth.

Sir David R. Hawkins, MD., PhD, and His Map of Consciousness®

Dr. Hawkins' work has been of particular interest to me because he is the only person who has described in detail 1) the process I went through in suicidal depression, 2) the trap of suffering with an eating disorder, as well as 3) the freedom I experienced in recovery. I have studied his work and watched countless hours of his lectures, getting to know the Map of Consciousness that he researched and published in 1995 for his book, *Power vs.*

Force. For copyright reasons, I cannot provide a picture of the Map of Consciousness or describe each individual level. This information is thoroughly depicted and described in *Power vs. Force* and other literature. For a complete history and biography of Dr. Hawkins, as well as information about the Map of Consciousness, go to www.veritaspub.com.

> **IMPORTANT:** This content is described in more detail in the book *Body Supremacy: Exploring the Torment of Eating Disorders as a Syndrome,* Chapter 3, pages 44-57

The Map of Consciousness incorporates "stages" of spiritual evolution that Dr. Hawkins identified as levels of awareness that correspond to an energy level of life within a range from 0–1000.[3] With each progressive rise in consciousness there is an increase in the "frequency" or "vibration" of energy and awareness that's experienced. Consciousness is impersonal as a person doesn't have a level of awareness unique to them. It isn't theirs. Rather, they experience a level of awareness that is also available to all other people. The map starts at the lowest and most primal stages of consciousness from 0–20, working up to the highest level of human consciousness of enlightenment at 700–1000.

Dr. Hawkins has described the lower stages of consciousness from 0–199 as elements of the narcissistic core of the ego that are self-serving and victim-oriented, and serve as the survival mechanisms of consciousness. This constricting, forceful, and negative self-centered consciousness was important and necessary for the evolution and survival of the species. However, it is also the source of fear, war, terror, and much suffering and psychological pain today and throughout history.

The Map of Consciousness describes the release from survival mode into more openminded ways of thinking and enlightenment, similar to Maslow's description of self-esteem and the progression into self-actualization. The positive levels of consciousness from 200–1000, are levels of independence, truth, and each degree progressively has more acceptance, compassion and lovingness towards all of life, as well as unconditional grace—as openness to all of reality.

In my mind, I visualize the higher levels of consciousness (which are freedom levels) in three parts:

1) Confidence and Exploration (200–399)
   - The first part of higher consciousness that Dr. Hawkins calibrated represents the *confidence, curiosity, and openminded willingness* to explore and expand human achievement and potential.

2) Love and Grace (400–599)
   - The second part of higher consciousness represents *the love, reverence, and devotion to all expressions of grace and compassion.* This is a shift from intellectual expansion to spiritual expansion. The third part represents the shift from and expansion of being "oneself" to being an expression and expansion of the whole and totality of life. For the purpose of this book, I will discuss only the first two parts.

3) Bliss and Enlightenment (600–1000)
   - The third part is far beyond my scope of awareness.

1) Confidence and Exploration (200–399)

The courage it takes to willfully expose the truth without controlling the outcome, even if the truth is death, allows a shift to occur that takes you out of the negative states of awareness to the expanding positive higher states of consciousness. I know for me, as I looked back at the horror that I almost committed suicide over, I could see my entire mind was trapped inside mechanisms that truly believed I would die. It was a compete lie.

However, the willingness to die, and the courage it took to accept the truth of people's judgment and abandonment in order to be free to be me, miraculously shifted my entire state of mind and way of experiencing life in a way that prior I didn't know existed.

When a person experiences this freedom, *the fear that held her hostage before loses credibility.* All of the energy she devoted inward toward self-preservation and survival is now shifted outward and freed to expand. Her mind focuses on the potential of life she has around her and what can be experienced, done, and accomplished which is a never-ending process.

I remember the excitement I had to go back to my job and school, and to make whatever I had work. There wasn't an ounce of fear of failure, but instead a curiosity to find out what could work with what I had. I was open to find out and willing to adjust and adapt to any outcome. Even if I ended up homeless, I had the competence, energy, and excitement for life to create and continue to explore endless possibilities.

NOTE: Dr. Hawkins describes these states as *forgiving, hopeful, harmonious, optimistic, trusting, and full of reason and understanding.*

As a person rises in onsciousness, she is motivated by truth, which is common in the academic environments. She seeks reason and understanding of the outside life and the universe we live in.

2) Love and Grace (400–599)

After my recovery I lived in a state of bliss for a period of about three years. It felt as if I was levitating in love and grace for all of life. At these levels of consciousness, life surrounding you illuminates and is brighter and more beautiful in its humble perfection. Everything is exactly the way it is supposed to be, even the struggle, pain, suffering, and anguish you see around you. There is context to suffering, and the innocence of all of life is obvious. There is a sense of lovingness that is heartfelt for all of life.

NOTE: Dr. Hawkins describes these states as *wise, understanding, reverent, serene, complete, loving, joyful, and full of peace.*

I believe it is these states of consciousness that are merciful, healing, and unconditionally loving. Beyond this are states of bliss that are difficult to describe. When a person has courage to surrender her life, and is willing to die in order to escape the bondage of survival mode, I believe higher states of consciousness are what give her the space to heal and repair her soul. The mercy of love and grace gives her a second chance.

Message from a YouTube follower in her 50s:
"You don't know me, but I am reaching out because I need to express my deep gratitude and appreciation for your work and for your words. Your words sparked the catalyst for my recovery. Nine days ago, my life shifted because of something you said in one of your YouTube videos. I am crying as I am typing this.

"My life has changed forever, and the immense gratitude I am feeling right now is indescribable. I am recovered and exploring my new world...my new life. I have been reborn. I will NEVER diet again. This feeling is incredible, and I will never go back to the hell of trying to change my physical body to feel better about myself to counteract the deep feelings of inadequacy and self-loathing. My soul is free. I cannot think of a greater gift. The words 'Thank you' seem inadequate, but it needs to be said. I would love to share my experience with you as a way to say thank you, and encourage you to continue your work, provide validation, inspiration and just express my gratitude."

Over the years, I've had the opportunity to observe full recovery from people who've suffered with eating disorders from all over the spectrum. I've also been able to witness continued struggles and frustration as people strain, gripping tightly onto their desires, and wanting to be thinner and diet, as well as wanting to eat as an emotional coping mechanism. One of the greatest blocks in people's recovery is when they think freedom is an all-or-nothing process.

For some people, freedom comes to them permanently and abruptly. For others, it comes in waves because of the different stages of humility the process requires.

More often than not, escaping and recovery is a trial-and-error process of letting go—like a battered woman that leaves and then returns to her abuser over and over again. It takes *letting go to know freedom does exist, and for some people it takes a return to suffering to get clarity about the truth, and to accept what needs to be surrendered, faced, and accepted.* As people go back and forth between freedom and suffering, when they give themselves grace and wiggle room to figure it out—eventually they clearly see the lies of the fantasy, and they finally let it go completely. This is the point when their mind is free to explore life, and they've learned they don't need or want another captor that keeps them trapped in fear and self-defense.

What it takes for a person to eventually get complete and total freedom, and then recovery, is unique to her personal willingness to face her own mortality, and to accept that by giving herself grace to figure it all out, she can handle it.

With courage to stop defending oneself from threats of rejection and abandonment that trigger her third hierarchy of need, she is set free from the need that's defining and controlling her mind. With courage to face survival threats to her "health" and body that trigger her first and second hierarchies of need, she is released from being a servant to fix or hide from those fears. When fear of her own body and food loses its power, and the anxiety and pressure to micromanage food, diet, exercise, and concepts of "health" lose importance—the mind is set free to be more rational and balanced about caring for her body.

By surrendering to the vulnerability of death, a person who previously was a prisoner to those survival mechanisms, is set free to determine for herself what's worth fighting and suffering for—and what isn't. This is the space of openness and freedom that exists after you escape, as well as the rebirth and recovery of your truth.

This quote from Haruki Murakami perfectly describes what I experienced once I surrendered my eating disorder survival and then recovered. My hope is that you, too, can come out of the storm different than the person who walked into it.

> *"And once the storm is over, you won't remember how you made it through, how you managed to survive. You won't even be sure, whether the storm is really over. But one thing is certain. When you come out of the storm, you won't be the same person who walked in. That's what this storm's all about."*

> – Japanese writer, Haruki Murakami

Recovery and the Expanse of Freedom

Personal Journal Entry from May 1998:

"I read an article today about the stages of eating disorder recovery. I was surprised because for me it happened so quickly. I assumed for others it must be just as miraculous as it 'just happens.' As I read through the article, I compared it to my own recovery, and I realize I did experience 'stages.'

"I remember both the denial and when I realized I needed help. I remember the day I decided it was up to me to quit and face my fear, and the day I saw myself and life around me as beautiful. My relationship with my parents and family are better than ever. And I've done nothing but grow and learn from my time suffering and then recovering.

"I've always been told that we are here to experience happiness and sadness, comfort and discomfort, hate and love—that without one, we cannot experience the other. I can honestly say this is true. Without my experience living in shame, and suffering with an eating disorder I couldn't have recognized the freedom and happiness that comes from self-acceptance and love.

"I believe every person will eventually have problems or face their own personal 'eating disorder.' It might be alcoholism, death of a loved one, the loss of a job or anything that causes grief. If they can accept the truth of their life, the pain does get better and the complicated times do pass, and they will experience a happier life. I know that if I can make it through the torture and hell of what I just recovered from, I can handle anything, and I'm ready for whatever hurdle I'll need to cross in my future. Although, I hope it doesn't come for a long while!

"If life was easy with no problems to struggle with and be sad

about, we wouldn't know what happiness is. People should be more excited (or at times more understanding) about our trials, because we only grow from them."

SECTION 4

Now What?

Message from 37-year-old woman with Binge Eating Disorder:
"Dear Robin, I just want to say thank you for saving my life. When I came to you for help, I was hopeless and desperate. Most of my life I struggled with binge-eating disorder, and finding you has given me a new life. It's been over a year now after our consultation, and I haven't binged since. Even more miraculous is that I have lost weight naturally and I don't care. For the first time since childhood, I haven't dieted, and I don't think of food the same way. Food no longer has any power except for satisfying my hunger in a delicious way. I am so lucky I got to know about you, and to talk to you. It was all worth it, and a life-changing experience…"

Three years later….
"Hello Robin, it's been almost three years since I spoke to you for that one and only session that has permanently changed my life. I am writing again to tell you how thankful I am for your help.

"I never imagined life can be this interesting, abundant, and intense without the diet cult-religion. Learning about hunger and food is a beautiful experience, like a field full of pleasures where I can pick

111

and choose and experiment with tastes, and also learn about my favorite meals, and what to feed this body that I live in and which works beautifully. The freedom you taught me is priceless. I'm not hiding in fear of bingeing or in shame because of my body. I feel a part of life as if I'm participating in the world. Again, can't thank you enough."

Chapter 7

Eating Without a Diet

"As a doctor, let me tell you what self-love does: It improves your hearing, your eyesight, lowers your blood pressure, increases pulmonary function, cardiac output, and helps wiring the musculature. So, if we had a rampant epidemic of self-love then our healthcare costs would go down dramatically...this isn't just some little frou-frou new age notion, 'oh love yourself, honey!' This is HARDCORE science."

– Dr. Christiane Northrop, author and authority in women's health and wellness

Telling the Truth

Defining what brings value and worth to the life you're living is your responsibility. When you give other people or belief systems the power to tell you what your life should be like and if you're worthy of living it, you are forfeiting freewill and independence to direct and define life for yourself.

It is your choice to give that power away, making your life an extension of the person or system given the power to direct and validate your life. Unfortunately, as strong controls and dictation are used to guide what and how to live, your inner sense of competence and ability to make decisions for yourself weakens. *The more you need others to tell you what and how you should be, the less aware you are of your own feelings.*

To recover your freedom, you'll have to take the reins to independently define the worth of your life, and what you want out of it, even when you might feel too immature and weak to know what you want or like. After recovery, it's common for a person to feel emotionally naked, like she has the emotional competence of a little child. I know for me, I wanted other's approval so much that I learned from an early age to transform myself to become what I thought others would like. I would study their mannerisms, the way they dressed and talked, and mirrored what they liked, hoping they'd like me. In doing so I lost touch with almost every aspect of my true self. After recovery, it felt like I had about as much self-awareness as a four-year-old.

> **I remember realizing that the only way to know what was right for my life was to be truthful to myself about myself, and to unapologetically accept whatever that was, in order to strengthen my personal sense of what I wanted for my life.**

To some degree, every person that I've worked with has felt a disconnect from themselves, as if their true self was a foreign stranger.

✓ When asked to get rid of the programs and concepts they've internalized about who they should be, their sense of themselves is blank or empty.

✓ They've lost touch with who and what they are.

✓ Instead of developing strength from an inner sense of themselves, their effort was harnessed outward to memorize and conform their identity to concepts of what they're supposed to be.

To recover from the suffering that comes from being that "fake persona," they'll have let those concepts go, and accept that they might get criticized for doing so, even when their sense of themselves feels immature and weak. They'll need to accept that truth without thinking there's something wrong with them or feeling bad about it. Moving forward, they'll need to take responsibility for expressing the nature of their true self and make decisions for what is right and truthful to them.

When I recovered, because I didn't know yet what it was that brought me excitement and motivation to live, I had to accept that I would have to figure it out without a plan to guide me, just like a developing child. I'd have to do this while people around me would make suggestions based on what's right for them, *as if it's right for me*. No matter how strong their opinion might be, I had to honor the truth of myself—even if it was weak and immature—before honoring the truth of someone else. This was the only way I could take ownership of my life and direct it in a way that didn't cause further psychological harm.

Taking ownership of your life comes with freedom and infinite possibilities, no different than a toddler starting life. Just as a young child learning the ins and outs of life, no matter what age you are when you choose independence, you too must learn the ins and outs of who you are and what you want with the life you're living. Just as a child will be criticized when she doesn't match societal dogmas like body image, you too must be open to being judged, ridiculed, bullied, and rejected when you honor yourself over the dogma you're seeking freedom from.

> **Instead of hiding and fighting in self-defense, recovery requires you accept the truth of yourself in exchange for freedom, even if it is seen as inferior.**

This freedom allows you to experience life from a new perspective; to see that your authentic value and ability to live isn't made better or worse when praised or judged by others when you're compared to self-"concepts" defined by a narcissistic culture.

Opening yourself up to life in order to face the honesty of yourself, no matter how other's respond, requires an incredible amount of courage and humility. Once the truth is made known, you are set free to be present with who and what you truthfully are, and you can naturally evolve without pretense or force. This means the emotional immaturity that occurs as a consequence when you're overly controlled, will need to be expressed and worked with in order to develop and mature. From that truth, the impulse and motivation to seek help outside of yourself instantly diminishes.

Accepting Weakness After Ending a Codependent Relationship

It's important that a person unapologetically accept the truth of her emotional competence, even if it is weak and immature. This is especially true if she's been personally controlling vulnerability with some form of behavioral or substance codependency. With respect to body image, accepting your true body frees you up to find other joys and pleasures in life that don't define your worth as a human, require excessive thoughts and focus, or force abusive behaviors. However, as those eating-disorder behaviors are removed, insecurities and emotional weaknesses that previously were sheltered will be exposed.

If you ate, exercised, or focused on food restrictions to cope with social anxiety, boredom, or some other uncomfortable emotion, *those feelings won't have a distraction or crutch when the previous coping mechanisms are surrendered.* To strengthen your capacity to handle emotions that you previously avoided in fear of failure, without distraction you'll have to accept and allow when and how they arise. This is the inevitable strengthening process that is required for anybody to grow up and develop a sense of competence and strength to handle the natural shifts, changes, and losses that are guaranteed in life—no matter how weak or immature you feel at the start.

> **Exposing yourself to the challenges that your eating disorder protected you from allows you to function from the truth of where you're at emotionally, and from there, you give yourself the opportunity to grow.**

I'm always amazed that a person who has developed a codependent relationship with emotional eating, exercise, and dieting doesn't recognize how her excessive need has removed freedom in her life. These needs might give her immediate relief, but these needs ultimately promote loneliness, sadness, discontent, and unhappiness. She's developed such an emotional dependence that she's lost touch with what it feels like to be emotionally free; to be able to create emotion without attaching those feelings to what aids her. She's relied heavily on her codependent relationship with the behaviors to give her emotional security, so that without them, she feels weak, fragile, and emotionally vulnerable. This makes it easy to sabotage any effort for independence, even if physical pain and illness is the obvious result.

In recovery, expect to feel moments of vulnerability as you let go of what had been controlling your emotional well-being. Your desire for emotional strength must be stronger than your fear of emotional destitution.

Wouldn't you love to enjoy the carefree, child-like, emotional creativity not defined by eating, exercise, or dieting?

Until you're willing to independently create inner emotional abundance, you'll always be seeking to find it *outside of yourself*. You will avoid what makes you feel defective, compensating for your feelings of emotional poverty, and sabotaging any uncomfortable effort for independence. Developing intrinsic, emotional sustainability is the key to unlock the chains of emotional addiction, and your imprisonment to body image, food, dieting, or exercise. For this you must have tolerance, humility, and a desire to create happiness for yourself—independently, without needing reinforcement.

Life Without Body Image, Weight Loss, a Diet, and Emotional Eating

One of the biggest vulnerabilities moving forward after letting go of body image is a person's dysfunctional relationship with food, dieting, and exercise that might have been used to cope with environmental stressors. For example, a person might have developed an emotional relationship with food and eating to cope with life stress, but only because she relied on the belief that a future diet would correct the consequential weight gain. When she gives up all forms of weight loss in order to recover, she'll have to rethink if she wants to continue to eat for emotional reasons when there's nothing to fix the permanent weight gain as the consequence.

For most people, without a diet they would never have connected *to eating as a way to cope* with insecurities in life. Therefore…

- When dieting and all methods of weight loss are removed, they are forced to face and address the emotions these behaviors aided or denied.

- After recovery, people are left to relearn how to eat and exercise without having the rules and regulations that stem from having to be a certain body image.

- After recovery, people have to live without the use of these behaviors to cope with outside stress in life.

- Without a diet and weight-loss method, you're guided by the signals of the body—and those signals can't be truthfully manipulated so that you can continue to cope with issues that need to be addressed and resolved in order to fully recover.

Eating Like a Child

I remind clients what it was like to be a child, to play for hours, and stopping only to eat when hunger couldn't be ignored. It reminds them of what it feels like to be emotionally liberated from food and dieting, when they didn't have guilt over what they ate—and how good it felt to be free from obsessing over what they eat and the physical ailments of under- and over-eating. When I describe what for me was a lifesaving childhood memory, they see some hope for redemption.

MY PERSONAL EXPERIENCE: When I was at my lowest point suffering with an eating disorder, I used to fantasize what it would be like to be a child again. One memory that I would visualize stands out. I was playing outside with my brother's plastic green army figures, giving each one a name as I lined them up. Some of the figures would die, and I'd bury them; others would march around and command other figures to do things. What made this memory so attractive to me? How I felt.

I was having so much fun creating with these toys that I vividly remember what it felt like to not want to come in for lunch. My mom called me in, but I just didn't want to stop playing. Eventually, when I could no longer ignore my hunger, I ran inside. Not wanting to waste another minute of my creative time eating, I didn't care what I ate, and ate very little of what Mom fixed. As I recalled the emotional freedom I had from food and dieting in this memory— the more I wanted it.

After recovery, I decided I would eat just like I was a child again.

1) *Food would be a priority when I felt true physical hunger.*

2) *If given the choice, I wouldn't hold off eating until I was too hungry and irritable.*

3) *I'd eat whatever I wanted without judging the food as "good" or "bad."*

4) *I'd eat adequately and avoid excessive physical discomfort from overeating.*

Rather than eat when I wasn't hungry, I'd find other things to do that were more appropriate and that provided purpose and pleasure to my day. This emotional freedom from eating, combined with the intrinsic use and trust of hunger, saved my life, and I haven't stopped "eating like a child."

Children don't want to be bothered to eat until they feel the physical irritability of hunger. As soon as that hunger is gone, they're off doing what they do best: playing, creating, and having fun. Doesn't that sound liberating, to be free from the torment of dieting guilt, and the incessant thinking about food?

When the stress and strain on our survival mechanisms geared toward preserving access to food is removed, our mind is freed to explore and create. As body image is removed, and our relationship with food liberated from those survival strains, many people struggle to understand when and how much to eat. They've forgotten the natural cues the body sends that regulates our food consumption.

I compare this sense to how the body sends signals letting us know we need to urinate. We get a physical sensation with a sense of time and urgency. When you first get the feeling you need to urinate, you don't necessarily need to go right then and there. We have the ability to override that sensation and wait until it's the right time with the appropriate privacy. The longer you wait, the more pressure you feel, and the more urgent the signal is in your mind. The hunger and the physical sensation guiding when you should eat is similar.

If there was a "urinating diet" regulating when and how much you should urinate, you'd have to ignore your body's natural signal, to instead mentally monitor conditions set by the system dictating a predictable pattern of urination. This sounds ridiculous, but when you look at the physical signals of hunger as an inborn regulation similar to urination, diets also seem ridiculous.

However, as people have relied on dieting regulation to control when, what, and how much they can and cannot eat, they've lost touch with these signals and how food affects them.

Chapter 8

Identifying Hunger—Your Ticket to Emotional and Physical Freedom

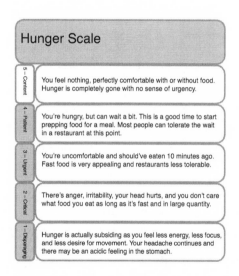

"Stop worrying about whether you're fat. You're not fat. Or, rather, you're sometimes a little bit fat, but who gives a shit? There is nothing more boring and fruitless than a woman lamenting the fact that her stomach is round. Feed yourself. Literally. The sort of people worthy of your love will love you more for this."

– Cheryl Strayed, *Brave Enough*, page 63

> **NOTE:** To make it easier for the reader, I've written three explanations for the science of hunger: Simple, User-Friendly, and Scientific. This chapter gives a simple explanation. In Chapter 11, I provide a more user-friendly version, as well as a more scientific explanation, written for doctors, practitioners, and people who are formally educated in cell biology and physiology. *All sources and researched referenced are listed at the end of the book..*

The Science Behind Hunger:
A Simple Explanation

To start, let's acknowledge the inherent difficulty of understanding the body's integrated system of organs, each requiring its own nourishment and energy demands, in addition to understanding the systems of tissues dependent upon these organs. The energy needed to sustain our organs and tissues is a system that feeds and depletes. It gives and takes from one organ to the next, all while accommodating the complex influence from both physical activity and food. This balance of energy demand and energy sharing is called *energy homeostasis*, and maintaining homeostasis sustains these integrated systems during both feast and famine.

All systems integrate fuel and energy demands not only daily, but over a lifetime. This constant striving for homeostasis is what stimulates the feelings of hunger that prompt us to eat, and to stop eating when we're satiated.

Hunger is one of our body's most important senses. Unlike the sense of sight, hearing, or taste, *hunger is a feeling we need in order to live.* It's the one physical sensation that tells us when our body needs fuel, and as hunger goes away, that fuel is no longer needed. Without hunger's physical discomfort, we'd have no desire to eat, and eventually we'd all die of starvation. On the other hand, if the feeling of hunger never subsided, we'd continually eat without getting relief from its physical irritation, which would also cause death.

For thousands of years, as food wasn't as predictably available and secure, hunger was an important physical cue that determined when eating was an imminent priority. As food was eaten, the cue to stop eating occurred when the feeling of hunger gradually disappeared. This helped keep food consumption to the minimal, efficiently preserving food rations for longer periods of time. People had to deal with hardship without food because excessive eating or eating without hunger wasn't an option.

Today, we have such an abundance of food that we can buy it whenever, for whatever reason, and in any quantity we want. Even though we don't live in a castle with chefs from all over the world providing enough food to overflow a table that can sit over 100 people, our entire culture and lifestyle is copious and plentiful *as if our world is the table of abundance.* We no longer need to farm for ourselves, preserve seasonally, or ration food among family members. However—because the weight-loss and diet industry over the course of the last century has pushed a large variety of diets, *many people have lost touch with the body's natural regulation to eat through the conscious awareness of hunger.*

Hunger has been ignored as an important physical feedback that dictates when eating is appropriate—and when it's not.

To eat functionally based on hunger, whether under forced rationing because of famine, or living in radical long-term abundance, you must understand the vital role hunger plays in guiding your body's primary need for food—as a hormonal stimulant.

Most people don't know that the fuel the body uses does not come from the food they just ate. Once you eat, a digestive process degrades the food, separates the vital nutrients from what's eventually removed from the body, and then it's stored into four different potential fuel sources:

1. Blood/cellular glucose,

2. Fat,

3. Glycogen, and

4. Body protein.

Of these four sources, we have no clue where the food will be stored, or when that fuel will be used. To make matters more complex, these four sources are not yet fuel. They are stored as "pre-fuel" or substrates that get converted into Adenosine Tri-Phosphate (ATP), or "fuel." ATP is to a human what gasoline is to a car—human gasoline.

The major difference is that ATP is not stored, but is immediately created from the breakdown of our stored "pre-fuel." Each of the four choices are special in that they provide ATP at different rates, different amounts, and uniquely, in different environments.

For example, *glycogen is a specialized fuel source that is converted into ATP very quickly,* like for a fast demand, such as when a runner sprints. However, in this circumstance, there's only enough to fuel the body for about 30-to-60 seconds.

Body protein can also be used, but is obviously not the body's first choice, since using muscles and tissue for fuel would weaken the entire body. Body protein is only available when all other sources are not meeting the body's fueling demands. This is a typical symptom of starvation.

That leaves us with *blood/cellular glucose and fat.* Which one do you think the body prefers to use? Most people answer, "blood glucose," but are surprised to hear the body actually does not want to use fuel from blood glucose, unless it has to. This is because blood glucose is the only fueling source for the brain. Brain cells don't have the ability to break down their contents to create fuel, like body protein, fat, and glycogen do. The brain doesn't have "gasoline-making" abilities, and therefore, needs fuel delivered to it. This is great news because if your brain could use its cell contents for fuel, we'd have a problem with brain loss similar to what occurs with fat or muscle loss. This is why blood must be regulated to provide the proper amount of glucose—not too much, which is toxic, and not too little, which can cause death.

If the body were to compete with the brain for glucose, you'd have only enough to supply fuel to the body for about 40 minutes. It would be essential that you ate sugar every 40 minutes to preserve the brain from having to compete with the body to survive.

Separate from the brain's needs, *blood/cellular glucose* is not sufficiently stocked to fuel the body's needs, which leaves the tedious role of fueling the entire body to body fat. Fat just happens to be the most effective and well-stocked fuel source needed to do the job effectively. Fat is the most effective source of ATP, as it can fuel the body of the average-sized human for about 30 days. In fact, fat is so effective at fueling the body with ATP that in a controlled environment, blood glucose could be completely reserved for just the brain and blood.

But to fully understand how the body preserves blood glucose for the brain when fat doesn't provide enough fuel, you must understand the hormones that influence the mechanism of starvation, and why the human body can live without food for a relatively long time.

Leptin's Role

When you compare all four potential fuel sources—blood/cellular glucose, fat, glycogen, and body protein—they all uniquely and circumstantially fuel the body in different amounts, and at different times. What determines which fuel source is used is highly linked to the hormone leptin. *Leptin is primarily a fat-derived hormone that was discovered in 1994.*

When elevated, leptin increases ATP production from fat cells—but if leptin levels decline, fat may not produce ATP at the rate the body needs it as fuel. If leptin is too low and fat can't supply adequate fuel, the body will tap into cellular and blood glucose.

As soon as the body begins to compete with the brain for glucose, mechanisms in the brain signal a defensive response. When leptin levels in the brain decline, in response to a rapid drop in blood glucose, enzymes become activated. These activated enzymes in the brain cause the physical irritation, agitation, and urgency to eat that our conscious mind feels as physical hunger.

This irritating signal to eat is for good reason—because food stimulates leptin.

When eaten, food in the mouth instantly stimulates the production of leptin, and as more food is eaten, each fat cell produces more leptin. As blood leptin levels rise significantly, fat can adequately break down to supply the body with ATP. In time, as blood glucose is restored to fuel the brain, and leptin levels increase, the enzymes in the brain that caused the urge to eat deactivates, and hunger subsides.

Q: What would happen if food were not eaten when the brain gives the signal of hunger?

A: Without food consumption to stimulate more leptin, glucose
would quickly deplete.

To prevent damage to the brain, there would be an increase in the breakdown of body protein (muscles and tissue), as well as stored glycogen. This
shift in fueling, although weakening to the body, prevents life-threatening
drops in blood glucose, and prioritizes fueling for the brain. The body responds with symptoms of starvation. Organs in the body that are stimulated
by leptin weaken their signal (thyroid), and others that are suppressed by
leptin over-activate (adrenals). Eventually this response establishes a new
equilibrium that requires less fuel, and less demand for leptin.

When you think about leptin, consider its vital role of allowing fat to supply
adequate fuel to the body in order to energize immediate physical demands,
but to also prevent starvation. You need to eat when the brain gives you
the green light that is hunger. However, if you eat without hunger, or eat
after hunger subsides, which is fullness, you may over-stimulate leptin,
and this can cause toxic levels of fuel, which can stress your responding
organs.

Too much leptin influences the entire endocrine system: over-stimulates
the thyroid, promotes hot flashes, sweating, adrenal fatigue, respiratory
problems, sleep disturbance, decreases libido, etc. Also, too much leptin can
over-stimulate fat's production of ATP.

**Fortunately, the body has mechanisms in place to prevent
death from this toxic response caused from eating food without the hormonal need—and it is called fat gain.**

Evidence suggests that when you combine excess ATP with an over-supply
of leptin, brand-new fat cells are born. These new cells are bigger and create
more leptin than the other cells.

Over time, with repeated bouts of too much leptin, more and more adipose cells accumulate, and eventually you *have fat gain in areas you never had fat before.* With each new cell, your fat produces more and more leptin, and as the new fat cells get bigger, the amount of leptin you stimulate grows exponentially.

This growth in leptin production significantly reduces the amount of food you need to balance your body's metabolic needs. This is like adding sound, not by increasing the volume to one speaker, but by adding more speakers; the sound becomes louder and louder as you add each new speaker. This magnification of sound is like the magnification of fuel from fat. If you have more fat cells, it takes less food to stimulate adequate leptin.

The more cells of fat you have, the more magnified the hormonal response to food, which means you can live longer eating less. This is a miracle! Fat gives you a great advantage if we had to ration in a famine because you would require significantly less food to reduce hunger, and you'd experience hunger less often. When under stress, a person's need for food reduces even more. Studies have shown that apparent vulnerability, perceived danger, or "survival mode" increases a person's leptin levels.

As a person senses a threat to her survival, whether it's a threat to her first, second, or third survival hierarchies of need, the brain sends a signal to stimulate an immediate supply of fuel for fight-or-flight mechanisms. It bypasses the need for food to stimulate leptin, because its inefficient to forage and hunt for food, and digestive energy takes away from the physical needs of body. Also, as stress stimulates leptin, when food is available and is eaten, the body is positioned to be more sensitive to fat gain, which would preserve more energy in case of future famine. Essentially when it's stressed, the body is more sensitive to fat gain no matter how "healthy" you eat.

> **IMPORTANT:** This response to survival mode when eating is discussed in detail in Chapter 8, "The Body in Survival Mode," of *Diet Supremacy: The Toxic Bond Between Shame, Dieting, and Emotional Eating.*

Even if there's no real danger, if a person thinks she's being threatened, her brain sends a signal to stimulate leptin—and an immediate supply of fuel is released to prepare her body for fight-or-flight survival mechanisms. If food is eaten during these times of perceived stress, her body is positioned to be more sensitive to fat gain, no matter how "healthy" she eats.

The survival benefit to this magnified leptin response to food and survival-mode stress is sensitivity to fat gain. Under such circumstances, fat gain allows your body to have more immediate fuel available to escape danger, especially when that danger is food shortage or famine.

Obviously, with more fat cells, you're going to get more leptin with stress even though you're eating less food. And…if you're not hungry and you eat anyway, your actions become the stimulus of leptin, whether your body needs it or not.

External Regulation with a Diet, or Internal Regulation with Hunger

The link between body fat and hunger shouldn't be surprising since we've known since the mid-1990s that leptin primarily comes from fat cells, and that it reduces hunger.

It's really quite simple: the more fat cells you have, the more leptin is produced when stimulated, which means you don't hormonally need as much food.

However, the difficulty with the science of leptin as it concerns the physical sense of hunger and fueling metabolism, is that it directly conflicts with externally regulated food intake. It disagrees with an entire weight-loss and diet industry that has capitalized and profited from telling people when, what, and how much to eat. As well, it also conflicts with eating out of habit, boredom, anger, sadness, celebration, and any other emotional reason.

While the food guide pyramid changes as the United States Department of Agriculture (USDA) continues to learn more about nutrition and the body's fueling mechanisms controlled by hormones, the diet industry continues to disperse information that may be encouraging even more fat gain.

The discovery of leptin and its role in fueling the body, completely conflicts with the outdated concept of monitoring how many calories we should eat based on assumptions about how many calories our body burns in a day. To make counting calories even less effective, we have no clue what fuel source the digested food will eventually restock, and when your body will use it. Calorie counting is a concept that we will look back at and understand why this method of weight loss was so ineffective. We'll wonder why we continued to spend hundreds of millions of dollars for diets to tell us when and how much to eat when no one has any idea how much fat we have, when we are hungry, or when food is needed hormonally.

In fact, predetermined mealtimes and pre-portioned food can predispose people to either under or overeat, or eat too late or too soon. To know how much and when a person should eat, would require you to know:

1. Exactly what her leptin levels are at all times,

2. How the environment and her stress levels impact her body's sensitivity to the food you choose for her to eat, and

3. The ideal range of leptin that signals to the brain and body that her available fuel meets her energy demands.

How does anyone know how many fat cells you have, how much leptin the food will stimulate, and if the amount of leptin is adequate, relative to the energy demand for that fuel?

> **NOTE:** Most people who have more body fat typically experi-
> ence hunger less often during the day. When they do feel hungry,
> it comes on quickly and intensely. This might be due to a more
> rapid drop in blood glucose, when leptin finally declines in the
> afternoon. This rapid hunger might be due to the incredible de-
> mand placed on blood glucose by this person's larger body size,
> as well as his or her need for more fuel than those who have
> smaller bodies. Again, leaner people typically experience hunger
> more often, eat more food, and have less comparable stress to
> their entire endocrine system when they eat more potent foods,
> like sugar, or eat much more than do people whose bodies con-
> tain more fat.

Eating "Bad" Food

When it comes to cravings or "emotional hunger," the feast-before-famine urges to eat that increase in anticipation of being deprived on a diet, can be a louder message than true physical hunger. When the food that is being restricted is more potent to stimulate leptin, like sugar, the prospective di-eter trying to lose excess fat will end up overeating those specific "bad" foods.

Candy, soda, and other sugar-based foods are highly potent for people who are stressed—and already have higher levels of leptin.

> **However, to demonize these foods as "bad," and suggest they be eliminated completely from a person's diet, inadvertently encourages people to binge on these foods before they are eliminated…and binge again when they break the diet rules, and again as they prepare to remove these foods the next time, and over and over again.**

When food is demonized as "bad," the person trying to restrict those foods will experience emotional stress if she eats said "bad" foods, and that emotional stress alone is a powerful stimulant of leptin. Therefore, when you combine the stress-induced leptin response with the sensitive leptin response to eating that "bad" food, together with the amount of food eaten, the dieter is guaranteed to be more sensitive to fat gain when compared to non-dieters who don't restrict food and aren't fearful or ashamed to eat the same exact "bad" food.

> **IMPORTANT:** You can read more about this in Section 2, "The War Between Feast and Famine," in *Diet Supremacy: The Toxic Bond Between Shame, Dieting, and Emotional Eating.*

True Physical Hunger

When you look at physical stress and illness associated with having extreme amounts of fat, it's easy to blame the fat, but now it's time to reconcile with the body. We need to recognize that our emotional stress about it, as well as the pendulum swing between dieting and overeating, has abused our built-in system of hormonal feedback, and that hunger has been ignored

Whether you've gained two hundred or ten pounds of fat be-cause of dieting and resultant emotional eating, to eat function-ally you have to listen to hunger, eat when it's present, and stop when it subsides.

Think about it:

- How often do you experience *true* physical hunger?

- How often does true physical hunger determine when and how much you eat?

- If you were to eat regulated by the physical sensations of hunger and fullness, how much food would you actually need to eat?

When hunger increases, your leptin levels are declining, and food, as a stim-ulant, is needed. As hunger subsides and leptin levels increase, food consump-tion is no longer appropriate. To follow hunger as a guide, you must be keenly aware how foods differently influence the speed and longevity of this signal. You can't compare—when, what, or how much others eat—to your body's needs. People that have no idea what real hunger feels like, find this difficult to understand, especially those who've lived their entire lives eating dysfunc-tionally by the dictation of diets and resultant emotional eating.

Again, this brings us back to using the physical feeling of hunger as a ra-tioning guide, and trusting that your body knows exactly how much it needs, and when. You can't compare your body's rhythm of hunger to any-one else's, since different types of food, as well as environmental and emo-tional stress combined with the number of fat cells you have, greatly influence the timing and need for food. Individually, you need to learn how to recognize physical hunger, and stop comparing it to the limitless reason-ing that is a normal part of our dysfunctional eating culture. This is like creating your own "abundant diet" rather the a "diet famine." You choose to eat based on the biological rhythms of hunger, not because you're forced to because of famine, but because you have the luxury and privilege to as a choice. For this to work, you have to know what true physical hunger feels like, apart from emotional need.

You can't compare your body's rhythm of hunger to anyone else, as different types of food combined with how many fat cells you have, greatly influence the timing and need for food hormonally.

Timed Eating and Breakfast

One of the most eye-opening observations I've made is why people who have more fat aren't hungry for breakfast.

When looking at the big picture, breakfast might be important nutritionally, but when hunger isn't present, it is not needed hormonally. Obviously if a person has less hunger, his or her hormonal need for food is less, which makes the nutritional value of what they do eat more important. But shouldn't hunger be the deciding factor of when and how much a person eats? Illness associated to chronic vitamin and mineral deprivation isn't the obvious concern when you compare it to the threat of chronic hormonal inflammation connected to overeating. The way we've interpreted the link between lack of breakfast and obesity has been backwards.

Ask yourself:

- Have you ever considered the reason people who have more body fat don't eat breakfast is because they're not hungry?

- Are you immediately hungry when you wake up?
- Do you force-feed breakfast because someone said it was

important, even though you are showing no reason to eat hormonally?

Need for breakfast should be solely based on hunger, similar to how we'd eat if we were rationing. The body *requires nutrition that food provides, but when you are eating without hunger, you're risking the balance of the entire endocrine system,* especially when you have more cells that magnify fat's fueling response.

- Could it be that when your melatonin level (a sleeping hormone) drops in the morning, your leptin levels conversely rise?

- Does it seem reasonable that this rise in blood leptin levels might be much higher for people who have more fat cells or more perceived problems and stress in their life?

- Could insatiable hunger in the middle of the night be triggered by the plunge in leptin or insulin, promoted by increased melatonin?

The research is available, and these questions have answers—the people who are treating illnesses associated with excess leptin just need to read about it. If you're not hungry in the morning, or when you're stressed, when you're bored, when you're tired, angry, or want to decompress…wait to eat until you are.

Physical Need—or Emotional Desire?

Differentiating physical hunger from emotional desires to eat that stems from body image is not as easy as it seems. Physical and emotional needs for food can become so intertwined that detaching one from the other can be difficult, and recognizing the difference, almost impossible. To make matters more difficult, years and years of dieting, as well as attaching judgment to food, can make a person feel incapable of deciding for herself what and how much to eat since she's learned to rely on others (like the weight-loss industry), for that information. Not only can this make her mistrust her body, and the food she eats, but she feels insecure without the restrictions of a judgmental diet.

Relearning to trust the physical cues of hunger requires that you let go of calorie counting, pre-portion-controlled foods, and pre-determined meal times. It demands that you end all emotional judgment about food. You must completely start over with your diet so you can develop confidence in your ability to listen to your body when eating—without the extreme opposites of our cultural excess, and without a diet's control.

The goal is to recognize how your body gives feedback, and to allow this feedback to guide when and how much food is needed, since varying foods influence this system differently. After you've mastered functional eating, the next goal would be to apply nutritional intelligence to the foods you choose. *To be successful, you need to focus on eating functionally before you attempt to learn to eat nutritionally.* This requires you to trust and learn to use your sense of hunger. This is where the hunger and fullness scale comes in handy.

Defining the Hunger and Fullness Scale

The hunger and fullness scale is a number scale (1–10) rating the sensation of hunger from 1–5, and rating fullness from 6–10. It is used to measure and define the physical sense of urgency to eat, as well as the degree and physical sensation of fullness after hunger is gone. It is a way for a person to assess the physical need to eat, which is regulated by the complex metabolic and hormonal systems of her body.

Rather than using memorized controls that the weight-loss and diet industry have formulated, controls that require continues mental reinforcement, the *hunger-and-fullness scale* allows your body to regulate food consumption based on natural physiological mechanisms that more closely match your body's metabolic needs. This allows your mind to have the freedom to explore other avenues of your life.

Because food is vital to life and central to our psychological wellbeing, using the rhythms and timing of hunger to direct eating allows your physical and psychological needs to be met, without straining your mind or body. Once a person lets go of body image, the hunger and fullness scale allows her to relearn what it's like to eat without the emotional drive and survival agitation of dieting. It gives her a clean backdrop to recognize the difference between physical need and the emotional drive to restrict or indulge. Learning these cues, and understanding what they mean, are an important step toward permanent recovery.

Here is description of each number on the hunger and fullness scale.

> **Hunger is described in terms of urgency,**
> **and *fullness* in terms of physical sensation.**

The Hunger Scale

1. *Disparaging.* Hunger is actually subsiding, as you feel less energy, less focus, and less desire for movement. Your headache continues, you feel lightheaded, and your stomach might have an acidic feeling. You're a bit cold, and your posture is lazy and rounded. You feel shaky, and a bit nauseous.

2. *Critical.* You have anger, irritability, your head hurts, and you don't care what food you eat as long as it's in large quantity—and fast (you're craving starches and sugars, combined with fat).

3. *Urgent.* You're uncomfortable, and you should have eaten ten minutes ago. Search for food is now imminent, as hunger is increasingly urgent, and choice of food is becoming less rational. Fast food is very appealing, and the wait time at traditional restaurants seem less tolerable.

4. *Patient.* You're hungry, but can wait a bit. This is a good time to start prepping food for a meal. Most people can tolerate the wait in a restaurant at this point.

5. *Content.* You feel nothing, perfectly comfortable with or without food. Hunger is completely gone, with no sense of urgency.

The Fullness Scale

6. *Satisfaction.* You are confident your hunger is gone. You are feeling good.

7. *Satiation.* You're feeling a bit too satisfied, burping, and feeling some discomfort in the belly. Because you have no hunger, continuing to eat would mean that you've justified it emotionally. This is usually when a dieter feels guilty, and may defend a compensatory binge.

8. *Full.* You're uncomfortable, and definitely feeling your stomach. There's still some room for food because your stomach hasn't started to stretch yet. Will need to wait three or more hours until your next meal.

9. *Discomfort.* You're very full, and feeling sick. Stomach is distended, with no more room for anything. Perhaps you

have indigestion and a headache, and wish to lie down to reduce discomfort.

10. *Pain.* You've eaten so much you're contemplating inducing yourself to vomit in order to relieve the physical pain. You have to unbutton the first button on your pants, and can hardly stand to move. You're tired and need to take a nap, making it feel like being "Thanksgiving full."

Here is an illustration showing the area of comfort without hunger or fullness, and also the areas of physical discomfort in hunger and in fullness.

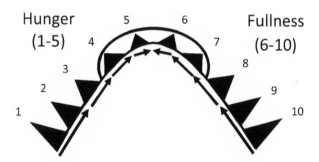

Hunger and Fullness Scale

This scale does not determine how fast one goes from feeling one number (disparaging) to the next. How quickly hunger elevates depends on the individual, and how much fat he or she has relative to stress and activity level. The same goes for how long a person goes without feeling hunger, and how much food a person needs to feel satisfied.

Many who have significantly more body fat don't feel hunger much at all, but when the physical urge to eat presents itself, hunger manifests rapidly and intensely. When food is eaten, it takes only small amounts of food, and satiation can last for longer periods of time.

For those who have less fat, it could take more time to adjust to hunger, but more food is needed to feel satisfied. This shows that with less fat, more food must be eaten to adequately stimulate enough leptin to desensitize the urge to eat that's sent from the brain.

Hunger is the communication to the conscious mind when food is hormonally necessary—and when it is not. In order to relearn the body's regulatory signals to eat, its imperative people pay attention to discern true hunger from mentally constructed diets and emotional desires to eat.

> **The goal is not to wait so long that you get too hungry—**
> **and not to eat too much so that you're overly full.**

In general, the idea is to start eating around 3.5 on the hunger scale, and stop eating around a 6.5-7.5 on the fullness scale. *There is no "perfect" way of eating to hunger and fullness.*

When a person recovers from an eating disorder and comes out of the brainwashing and strictness of dieting and compensatory bingeing, it's important she give herself grace and lenience to figure this out. Similar to a child learning the signals of the need to urinate, and then is potty trained, a person must give herself adequate time and practice to learn the signals of hunger, how her body responds to a large variety of food, and the physical sensations of satiation. Without that grace, she is likely to return to dieting and the misery and dysfunction she is wanting to recover from.

Email from a woman in her 40s:

"I wanted to let you know how important your videos discussing the hunger scale was for me. I started dieting in high school and have been on and off a diet since. When I'm not dieting, I'm bingeing and getting ready to start the next diet. I've done every diet and weight-loss program that has ever existed, including bootcamps and personal trainers. You name it…I've done it. I came across your YouTube channel when someone posted one of your videos in an emotional eating group. You were describing the hunger scale and how you used it to recover from an eating disorder. I decided to try it myself, and it has changed my life.

"It was hard to start because I was still judging food as good/bad. But as I did what you said—I stopped worrying about my weight, stopped judging food, and focused my energy toward learning hunger and the feelings of fullness, I have felt so free!!! I've never been so relaxed around food, and I've stopped binge-ing completely. One thing I wasn't expecting was how much better I feel…even when I eat food I used to think was bad. I don't think about food all the time, and I'm not afraid to eat anymore.

"I'm far from perfect, but I'm in a way-better place than when I was all-or-nothing dieting. I can't believe how many DECADES I wasted when I could've listened to my body and been FREE. I'm so grateful for you and the information you are sharing out there."

SECTION 5

Relearning How to Eat

Messages of Hope

Woman in Her 50s Struggling
with Body Image and Emotional Eating

Message: "If I hadn't stumbled upon your YouTube channel, I could have easily stumbled upon a diet, and I'd still be suffering in the same crazy cycle. I've learned so much from working with you, and because of that, my life has had major changes. I can say that I am much happier now that my weight doesn't define me, even though I was depressed about it for decades. I don't carry judgment about how I'm supposed to be, and the critical nature of what "beauty" is supposed to be. And I am no longer wasting time, energy, and money worrying about my weight or the food I'm eating. Thanks to your wisdom and help, I don't label food as good or bad anymore. I'm so grateful to have found you and this freedom."

Woman in Her 60s Struggling
with Body Image and Emotional Eating

Message: "I met Robin after someone recommended that I read her book and watch her YouTube videos. After hearing her talk to other people struggling with emotional eating, I decided I wanted her help. The work we did together was unbelievable. Robin, thank you for helping me realize my relationship with food was connected to other aspects of my life. I learned so much about myself, and it has been life changing. It has been over five years since we've worked together, and I am still free from dieting, emotional eating, and worrying about my weight."

A Woman in Her 30s

Message: "I found Robin on YouTube and tried to stop bingeing with the use of the hunger and fullness scale. I continued to struggle so I decided to bite the bullet and work with Robin. I like the way she tells it like it is, doesn't placate your issues, and puts your issues in the spotlight. After the first consultation I wasn't sure I was ready to let go of wanting to be thinner. I decided to continue to work with her, and again after a few sessions, I wanted to quit because it was so hard and difficult to face letting go of all the things I wanted to achieve from losing weight. However, the more I suffered bingeing and my frequent running back to diets, the more I realized what Robin was saying was the truth. Once I realized I had to let it go, I cried and cried. It was like a light bulb that switched on, and it was easy after that. It took a good year of work with Robin before that moment happened—and it changed my life."

Chapter 9

The Table of Scarcity or Abundance

"The opposite of scarcity is not abundance. It is enough."

– Brene Brown, Scientist and Author

The "Hunger-Scale Diet"

For many people, years of chronic dieting bring to the hunger scale their feelings of emotional hardship with their body—and a history of resentments for having been deprived over and over again.

Old grudges, like having to control or limit food as a child, are projected onto feeling controlled with food. Consequently, no matter how freeing and healing eating to hunger might be, the resentment for having to be guided by the body can feel like being controlled and restricted, especially if there's hope for weight loss as a result. It can make eating based on the regulation of hunger fullness fell like punishment.

While observing people learning how to eat based on the body's rhythms of hunger, I've found that it's extremely difficult to learn whether they still hold themselves to a body image. When she's afraid of weight gain, or "unhealth," she will continue to judge and demonize food as "dangerous." I believe this triggers insecurity to her first hierarchy of survival needs, and this distorts her perceptions of food as the enemy. The result is:

1. She becomes very strict in following the hunger scale. She won't allow herself to eat past 5, and ends up complaining that she is hungry all the time, and will continue to overeat as a result.

2. She labels food as "good" or "bad," which puts her in a position to have to negotiate for food and eat emotionally. For example, a person will negotiate with her judgment of cookies as bad, that she can safely eat one cookie—but because she isn't listening to her body to determine the quantity of cookies, she will end up eating far more than

she initially intended. Because of this, she overshoots her hunger, resulting in too much fullness.

3. The food judgments and rules promote fears and anxiety when a person eats, thus disrupting her ability to discern hunger. Once a person has anxiety about food, it's almost impossible to discern physical hunger because the fight-or-flight mechanisms turn off those signals.

When a person is still fearful about her weight and body image, she projects that fear onto food, and her *willingness to listen to hunger diminishes.*

To be honest, I have never seen the hunger and fullness scale work for people who still hold fear-based body images—especially people who are afraid of weight gain and being "unhealthy." The hunger scale isn't perfectionistic or strict enough to meet the needs of her fears.

The problem is that the intensity of a person's body image expectations get projected onto staying perfectly inside the space of not being too hunger and not getting too full. It comes across in the mind as tension or "stress." This increases the pressure for her to be perfect, which promotes an unforgiving all-or-nothing approach. If there is overeating, even if it's minor, her mind equates it to complete failure, which increases her risk of bingeing and trying to undereat later.

In order for the use of the hunger scale to provide relief, she will need freedom from body image so she can learn to distinguish hunger and satiation without the stress and pressure of perfectionism. Like any skill that is developed, it takes trial, error, patience, and practice. When a person gives herself the space to learn her body's cues of hunger and fullness, the process is relaxed and allowed to progress naturally.

Eating Without a Diet: Radical Abundance or Famine and Rationing

There are two ways I help people get a sense of what it's like to eat unregulated by a diet, and regulated by the physical cues of hunger and fullness.

1. Eating as if you have perpetual excessive abundance of food forever.

2. Eating as if you must ration food because of environmentally forced famine.

Famine and Rationing

Visualize how you would eat to conserve food to feed yourself and your family for a month, without the option of getting more. I imagine this is what it would be like harvesting food in the fall, and preparing to preserve what you have to last through the winter months.

- How would you ration the food daily?

- What reason would make eating appropriate?

- Would you eat until you felt uncomfortably full?

- Would you eat without hunger for emotional reasons?

- Would you force yourself and others to clean their plates, or to save what's extra to be eaten later?

- Would you let yourself get so hungry you'd irrationally eat more than you needed?

To preserve food, you'd eat only when there was some hunger, but not too much. Then you'd eat only until that hunger was eased, but not a bite more.

- What would you do when bored?

- How would you celebrate if there wasn't enough food?

- Would you need a reward for not overeating?

When I ask my clients these questions, the answers are predictable. Most feel they'd be grateful as long as they had enough food to keep themselves and their family alive. They almost always point to hunger as a guiding sense about when to eat and how to instinctively avoid overeating. From this viewpoint, food is seen functionally as an important requirement for life.

The extra relationships and roles that eating and dieting play are only relevant because we have an overabundance of food, and haven't had to relate to food in a realistic life-or-death manner. Even in anorexia, restricting food is a privilege and choice when we have food overflowing and continuously available. Dieting isn't forced and out of a person's control because of a cataclysmic famine. It is a choice—however it doesn't seem that way when it's necessary to survive a culture that narcissistically worships thinness.

Mentally visualizing a famine scenario forces a person to independently assess her emotional strength, when eating emotionally isn't an option. For most, a sense of emotional strength and confidence is instantaneous when she has no alternative.

The question we need to answer is: Do we really need something cataclysmic and famine to force us to face what our lives would be like if emotional eating wasn't an option, and if food restrictions weren't superficially reinforced?

If you choose to eat functionally based on the body's regulation through the sense of hunger and satiation, you'll need to do it even though food is at all times abundant, instantly replenishable, and easy to access.

Eating in Radical Abundance

Today, food is easy to get, in any quantity, and is relatively affordable for most people. The ability to cope and hide from our fears and stresses with food has become an easy distraction—especially in a culture that pushes food restrictions while living in that abundance.

As people have relied on dieting and food restrictions to guide their eating, they've also triggered famine mechanisms while food is available and abundant around them. This has enabled people who diet to develop an emotional reliance on food in order to give themselves temporary relief from the survival strains of dieting.

> **Over time, as they develop a connection between certain emotions and the freedom to eat, they become more and more emotionally reliant on eating to cope with the vulnerabilities of life. As a result, they weaken their innate sense of self-esteem and tolerance for life's normal stress. Food becomes a central focus and need in life for emotional reasons, and at the same time is perceived as a threat for physical reasons.**

When I ask clients how they'd eat if there weren't any forms of diet regulation or restrictions, most people respond that they'd have fear they wouldn't know what to do. They assume that if given access to the available abundance of food around them, they'd eat excessively without end. They're afraid when given access to food they won't know when to stop. However, this fear arises based on their history and what they've experienced in their past with eating compulsions that stem from the severity of their diet's restrictions and rules.

I recall having the same initial assumption, but as I thoroughly thought through what would truthfully happen, I realized that without a diet the mechanisms that drove my impulsive binge episodes would no longer be there. As the thin(ner)-supremacy body image is surrendered, so are biased needs for dieting, as well as the artificial threats and dangers to a person's first hierarchy of survival needs. Without the diet regulation, these survival mode impulses to secure food go away.

As dieting and fear-based food judgments and restrictions about food are removed, *there are no rules and regulations that dogmatically decide:*

- How much or how little you should eat.

- The timing of when you should and shouldn't eat.

- What foods are "safe" or "dangerous," "good" or "bad," or "right" or "wrong" to eat.

By eliminating these regulations, a person:

- Doesn't need to use emotional reasons to negotiate, plead, and bargain with the diet rules for why she deserves access to food.

- Doesn't need emotional eating to serve as a break from the strain of diets.

- No longer has rules that when broken, lead to feelings of failure, loss, and shame. Without dieting rules, there is nothing to "break" or ruin.

- Doesn't have a way to fix consequential weight gain that occurs as a result from emotionally driven eating. There's nothing to enable the emotionally codependent nature of emotional eating by taking away the consequences. There's no "fall guy" to fix the physical impact and weight gain that occurs when eating is negotiated for emotional reasons. This means that if she chooses to eat to hide from an emotional challenge, she is accepting the physical consequence as a permanent result, putting her into a position to recognize her response comes at a cost.

- Doesn't have to eat more or eat available food all at once in fear she won't get more. The food isn't going away, and more is always available. There's no future or anticipated deprivation around the corner that triggers a need to eat just because it's available. For example, just because peanuts or pretzels are offered when flying in an airplane, that doesn't mean you have to eat them right then and there. You can get pretzels and peanuts any time you want, which makes them less "special."

When body image is surrendered, there is no reason for weight loss-oriented deprivations and food regulation. Without those regulations, many people feel incredible liberation, but that freedom comes with open abundance of food that saturates our current modern society.

Without a diet to regulate and direct when, how much, and what you can and cannot eat, a person is left to figure out how she's going to eat moving forward. Besides teaching a person to look at how she'd eat if she had to ration her food, I also teach her to eat as if she is given permanent access to "the table of abundance."

The Table of Abundance

Imagine that you win the lottery, and you purchase a large mansion for your family to live in for the rest of your life. In this mansion is a huge dining hall with chefs from around the world cooking for you daily. In the dining hall is a very long table that could host over 100 people, and on this table are overflowing amounts of food. There's fruits and vegetables of every variety, breads, pastries, cakes, pies, pastas, chocolates, candy, lentils, rice, seafood, and meats and cheeses of every kind from all over the globe. Whatever you want is there every day, all day long, in endless quantity for the rest of your life. I call this the table of abundance. It is overflowing and will stay that way for centuries to come.

When I describe this table to clients, I get a couple of reactions. Most of the time people feel a little overwhelmed and grossed out by the excessive richness of the table. They immediately feel a calm separation occur as they realize that the food is there every day, all the time, and that it gets restocked as soon as something is eaten. There's a sense of separation that occurs as they don't have to think about food or hold food in their mind as a central focus any more. If they know they can choose whatever they want when they need it, they don't have to worry about it, and they don't have to waste their day stressed about whether there's going to be enough.

A less-common initial response is pure excitement when I describe the table of abundance, but that excitement subsides as they realize that the food would eventually lose its appeal.

At first, some people assume they'd spend all day every day eating as their central focus, and because of that they assume this table of abundance is a bad thing. However, when they truthfully imagine what would actually happen, they realize the food on the table of abundance allows them to relax as its availability has no end. The food and the perpetual abundance on the table loses its "specialness."

I ask each person how her life would change and what she'd do with her time if she always had such overflowing abundance at her fingertips. Most people feel great relief knowing with that type of food security, they'd relax about food and let their minds be liberated to focus on other things. Eating would only be exciting when they were hungry.

Without hunger, they'd find other things to do with their energy and time because they'd know that when it's time to eat, the food will be available in all its variety and plenty. They won't miss out, not get any, or go hungry. Because the overflowing abundance will always be available, there's no pressure to eat as much as they can in one sitting because it will be available the next time they're hungry—for the rest of their life. Eating one item doesn't mean they'll never get a different item or are missing out. Everything on the table will be available again and again and again, day after day after day. If there's pizza available every day, it doesn't make sense to eat excessively thinking you won't have enough or can't get it later. *The emotional reasoning behind overeating loses power.*

When I bring up emotionally based eating in regard to the table of abundance, people recognize the unusual nature of emotional eating when food is always abundant and available without needing to beg for it.

Unless there is a true famine, or foreseen loss of food in the near future, any reasoning to excessively eat at the table of abundance when there isn't any hunger or physical need would be clear indication of an emotional problem, or some sort of trigger of survival mode.

And because there is no diet or reinforced food judgments and restrictions, the choice to excessively eat for emotional reasons comes with accepting full responsibility for the resultant weight gain and physical consequences.

When access to food is fully and completely safe and secure for the long-foreseen future, the need to eat based on survival-securing impulses goes away. The relaxed and less forceful need to eat for hunger and pleasure become a stronger motivation, and all of the energy and focus that used to fixate on food and food restraints, is freed up to explore other possibilities in life.

The freedom that opens up when dieting and food aren't the main priority or central focus in life leaves people at a loss for what to do with their time, mind, and energy. This freedom is why many people sabotage their own efforts to change, even though the result is both more suffering, and living a predictable life they know harms them. Holding onto old patterns of thought that sensationalize emotional reward from studying diets or eating as entertainment make the recovery process very difficult. For most people, the creative process is difficult because it requires that you let go of old ways of thinking to create something new. To do this, you have to create new hobbies and find new ways to entertain yourself that don't require eating.

Ask yourself:

- If eating, over-exercising, or studying diets weren't an option, what would you do to fill your time?

- Would you start or finish a project?

For many people, once body image, dieting and excessive food consumption are removed from their life, they feel as if they're young children learning who they are and how to live again. Learning how to eat without a mental concept regulating their food consumption can seem scary—especially when dieting and food controls have dictated their relationship with food and directed how they should eat for most of their life. *However, as body image is removed from the equation, a person has the space and grace to learn and figure it out.*

Without having the pressure to regulate her body fat, there's no stress, pressure, or perfectionism demanding she strictly diet without lenience. From there she has a tension-free environment to learn her body and the physical cues it sends as a way to regulate when food is physiologically needed. With time and practice she can reconnect with her physical sense of hunger and satiation, to naturally guide when and how much she should eat, freeing her energy and mind from having to mentally manage it.

Message from follower recovering from anorexia, bulimia, and binge eating disorder:

"I am always amazed by how much food my body may want when I am ovulating/on my period. Today has been a very hungry day and I must have three solid (and generous) meals and two snacks on top. I have been insatiable all day (even after drinking water). All food has tasted delicious and I finally feel somewhat comfortable. It is amazing how the appetite amps up or diminishes depending on various factors, and it is honestly a wonderful mechanism. There is something so perfect about it. I used to feel so guilty for being hungry, but now I take it in my stride and enjoy all the wonderful food available to me! It also horrifies me that I used to restrict my food SO much, and to the same level EVERY day. No wonder I was binge eating! I used to eat less than 1000 calories some days,

and now I'm not even sure what I eat (I don't count) but it's easily over double that. It brings tears to my eyes to think that we do this to ourselves; we're only here a short time and we torture ourselves unnecessarily for goals we're brainwashed to want. I hope everyone is feeding their hunger and taking care of themselves."

—————————————————

Chapter 10

The Mind:Body Method:
An Attempt to Structure
a Recovery Process

"The single most vital step on your journey to enlightenment is this: learn to disidentify from your mind."

– Eckhart Tolle

The most difficult task for me, besides verbalizing what it feels like to suffer inside an eating disorder, has been trying to organize a recovery process so that there's a consistent and predictable approach to present to other suffering people. Although recovery is similar for many people, each and every person I've worked with didn't necessarily follow the same route to recovery.

The strictness that they hold themselves to related to body image is different, the type of body image they are seeking varies, and the intensity that they've coped with when dieting and binge eating is different. People have different meanings for the images they want from their body, and the level of fear they experience in letting it go can be more or less intense, depending on how much they've suffered trying to achieve it. There is a spectrum from the extreme of anorexia and orthorexia, to different forms of bulimia, to emotional eating, and the opposite extreme of binge- eating disorder or "food addiction."

> **IMPORTANT:** This content is described in chapter 9, "Trapped Inside Body-Diet Supremacy Syndrome", in the book *Body Supremacy: Exploring the Torment of Eating Disorders as a Syndrome.*

For some people who've suffered so intensely that their body has grown to a size that has resulted in permanent ailments and limitations, letting go of their codependent coping mechanisms to eat can be extremely difficult. The larger a person is, and the more physical limitations and ailments she has because of her size, can make it much harder to accept her body. To accept her body means she must accept the physical ailments and fears she might die sooner—especially when a person with binge eating disorder stops dieting in order to recover.

NOTE: This is especially significant when her doctors and medical support (who don't know of her eating disorder) are encouraging her to radically diet.

The approach to recovery for this person is going to be at a different angle than the approach and angle taken to help a person who is starving herself, and who lives in isolation trying to maintain her thinner body away from the "fattening" threats of losing control with food. The process isn't an exact science, and it isn't necessarily the same for each person.

However, over the years, as I've tried to process my recovery after the fact—and then I monitored and coached hundreds of people—I've noticed that some aspects of recovery are very predictable.

In this chapter, I am presenting my attempt to structure a process for people to follow when they are ready and willing to escape and recover. Clearly, I'm not aware of what I don't know yet and what I'm still learning. Because of that, I'm certain this information isn't adequate or complete enough, and I expect this process will improve and change as other people add their expertise, and as I learn more. For the sake of putting it on paper today, I will communicate what I am aware of now, knowing full well that sometime in the future this information will evolve.

To start, I call this process of recovery from "body-image syndrome" and resulting disordered-eating *the Mind:Body Method*. To describe this method, I will split this chapter into two sections. The first will discuss the Mind of the Method, and the second the Body of the Method.

The Mind:Body Method

Overall, people feel hope and confidence that the concept of using hunger and fullness as a guide to when, and how much to eat will relieve them from having their mind fixated on food and dieting. They are excited by the notion that the body can do the job of directing food intake, which gives them a sense of relief and freedom—like getting out of jail—to explore the life they want to live.

Over the years, I've seen predictable trends when helping people through the process of learning to eat based on the rhythms of hunger. To start, many people adjust their willingness to rely on their body's hunger rhythms to guide them, depending on how important their weight is.

- No matter how refined, accurate, and aware a person becomes of fullness and hunger, fear of weight gain diminishes her sense of hunger and negates her willingness to follow it.

- When a person's emotions and strictness about her weight increase, understandably there's a decrease in her sense, ability, and choice to follow her body's hunger rhythms— in fact, *she is afraid to follow it.*

- Underlying strain with her body and her desire to be and stay thinner, promotes anxiety and fear about food— which fosters a difficult, and often-impossible environment for her to relax in order to learn and discern hunger and fullness.

- As a person feels bad about her weight or weight gain, food becomes a threat, and the first thing she'll do is emotionally overeat in preparation for a diet.

The link between body image, fear of food, and difficulty eating to hunger became increasingly more obvious as I worked with more and more people—to the point where I could predictably sense when a person was going to struggle with food and eating based on the degree of emotional strain she had with her weight and size.

For some people, what spurs emotional issues with food isn't fear of weight gain, but it's emotional excitement and success attached to weight loss. If a person symbolizes success or pride to when her body loses body fat, this often puts pressure on her to be stricter with the process, essentially making the hunger and fullness scale a "diet." As a result, she is vulnerable to compensatory overeating if she isn't able to perfectly perform or eat to hunger.

Another reason I've seen people overeat—the pride and success attached to weight loss is the connection between reward eating and weight-loss success—as if extra eating is a way to reward herself. The end goal of eating, based on the biological rhythm of hunger and fullness became irrelevant the more emotional that participants were about being thinner, losing weight, and keeping off the weight they lost. However, when people were indifferent about weight loss or weight gain, eating to hunger came naturally.

I found that 1) by initially prioritizing and addressing body image, and then 2) adequately practicing eating based on the rhythms of hunger, there was a radical reduction in the likelihood that the person would revert back to old patterns of dieting and emotional eating. Permanent relief and freedom from body image gave her equally permanent freedom from both disordered-eating and weight-loss behaviors.

The Hunger and Fullness Scale

The hunger and fullness scale is an essential tool to help a person learn her physical cues to eat as well as cues for when to stop eating. This is unique to each person's body. No single mentally constructed diet can determine an individual's relative hormonal needs for food. This is why discerning hunger and fullness is essential in helping each person to understand her own body's needs.

A 39-year-old Client Tells Her Story:

"I started to feel bad about my body around the age of 10 due to classmates making fun of my size, which at the time was in a healthy range. I started to sneak extra snacks and desired the most-unhealthy food since I made food the enemy. As I got older, I tried numerous diets with my mother and friends, and was "successful" in losing 100–150 pounds three separate times. When I found myself bigger than ever and struggling to lose weight, I desperately searched YouTube for help with my binge-eating disorder that I assumed I must have. Someone suggested I watch one of Robin's videos, so I took a chance listening to it.

"Through watching her videos and by working with her, I've learned that the human mind is designed to desire more food if you are telling it that food will soon become scarce when you start your diet. As long as I continue to believe that I need to lose weight, I will continue to overeat.

> ***"My body is not actually the problem. The problem is believing the diet industry and society that encouraged me to believe that my body is the problem, and that it needs to be fixed."***

"The hunger and fullness scale has helped me to not worry about when to eat or how much to eat. So much time has been wasted in the past worrying about food and which types of food are "good" or "bad," and what time of day you're expected to eat, when none of that matters as much as trusting your body to know when it's need-

ing nutrients. It's like pressing the reset button on learning how to eat the way our bodies were meant to."

To start, I recommend:

- Keeping track of your hunger rhythms during the day,

- Recording the time hunger arises,

- Recording the type of food you choose to eat, and

- Noting the coordinating number from the hunger and fullness sides of the scale that matches when you started eating and when you stopped.

The reasons aren't to "control" your food consumption, but it is to remind you that your body is regulating your eating patterns. When having to log the body's hunger rhythms, it helps a person recognize the difference between what are her emotional wants, and what are her body's physical needs for food. It is a way to observe the truth of her body compared to her emotional impulses to restrict or emotionally eat food.

The most important assessments are 1) where you are on these scales before you eat, and 2) being able to determine when to stop eating. The goal is to stay within a physically comfortable range on the hunger scale, avoiding both low numbers of extreme hunger and high numbers of extreme fullness.

Your goal is to do the same thing as a child who is too busy to eat until her hunger becomes uncomfortable—she stops playing, eats just enough for the hunger to go away, and to have enough energy to continues what she was doing before.

Confidence is built as the body becomes predictable. This predictability is learned by tracking the body's hunger signals using time, what, and how much you eat—and limiting yourself between 3.5 and 6.5.

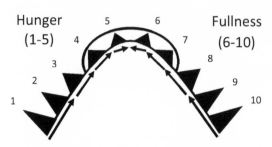

Hunger and Fullness Scale

Here is an example log of one of my days, using the hunger scale. Some days I eat more, other days I eat less. There are days when I don't get hungry until after noon, and the amount of food it takes to feel satiated always varies. Eventually, as a person identifies these signals with confidence, the need goes away to log in everything to remind her to follow these signals.

Time	Meal	Hunger Scale Number	Before/After
7:00	Coffee with cream	4.5 /	5.0
10:15	Breakfast	3.5 /	5.75
11:35	Snack	4.0 /	4.75
1:00	Lunch	3.5 /	7.0
3:40	Snack	4.0 /	5.25
6:00	Dinner	3.25 /	6.25
8:30	Snack	4.5 /	5.5

To make eating functional, allow yourself to eat what you want without judgment, and limit quantity, using the body's signal.

Preparation is extremely important when relearning how to eat based on hunger and fullness, especially vital for those with busy schedules. The key to not getting overly hungry is doing the best you can to have food on hand or easily accessible when hunger presents itself. However, if you find you've become too hungry, take it as an opportunity to observe how the signals of hunger intensify.

This approach to eating completely personalizes when and how much to eat, all the while keeping track of what food affects your appetite throughout the day. For example, we suggest you eat breakfast when you feel hungry. For many of us, this isn't until a couple of hours after waking, thus you may make lunch a smaller meal. Some people who exercise notice their hunger changes after their workout, with either an increasing or decreasing appetite. The choice to eat is completely based on hunger, and stopping food consumption is based on *removal of hunger, not fullness.*

The goal is to end the need for a diet forever by using the cues of hunger and satiation to guide eating, eliminating the justification to eat without a physical need for emotional reasons, and to gain emotional strength through autonomy.

No matter how simple and freeing eating is, if based on the rhythms of hunger and fullness, it is your choice and responsibility to tell yourself the truth. When responsibility is taken, and the body is given the reins to determine when and how much a person will eat, freedom from having to focus on it and worry about the outcome is a natural consequence. This process gives you an opportunity to break away from a life defined by the condition of your body, fears of food, and impulses to eat emotionally, in order to live open to life and its infinite potential. The result is emotional strength, independence, and a mind and body set free from the torments of abuse.

Part I

The Mind of the Method

*Tackling Body Image Before Addressing
the Hunger and Fullness Scale*

The "Mind" of the Method

The "Mind" objectives of the Mind:Body Method are to:

1. Identify narcissistic body-image ideals and parameters you compare your body to.

2. Identify beliefs and symbolisms attached to these body-image parameters.

3. Permanently let go of the symbolisms and benefits attached to the body image.

4. Accept the body unconditionally, for what it naturally is.

5. Agree to independently navigate the freedom in your life that arises after the body image is let go.

As a person's underlying emotional strain with body fat and her emotional charge to be thinner is resolved, fear about food diminishes, and she will have an easier time discerning and relying on hunger to guide her eating. It is only then that she has a relaxed and natural environment that allows her the grace of figuring it out and learning what it's like to eat based on hunger rhythms.

The intention of the "Mind" in the Mind:Body Method is to guide a person to diminish the mind control and role that body image plays in how she relates to her life. The end goal is that she is indifferent about and accepts the natural conditions of her body so that her body isn't perceived as a dangerous enemy, triggering primitive survival mechanisms encouraging the need to diet in self-defense. Ultimately, the goal is to diminish the sense of survival safety and security attached to being thinner or any body image, and to remove the requirement of being thinner from her identity and concept of "health."

For some people, it can take over a month, sometimes two to three months, of letting go of body image before they can focus on the hunger and fullness scale. For others, letting go of body image can happen in a solitary moment, or it can take years. It's a matter of whether she's suffered enough to be willing to let it go.

When a person feels indifferent about the conditions of her body, as well as the potential weight-gain or weight-loss changes that her body will experience in life, the foundation of internal work needed to detach body image from the expectations they have for their body is complete. It is from this point a person can effectively address any residual emotional relationships with food that might still exist.

OBJECTIVE 1:

Identify narcissistic body-image ideals and parameters you compare your body to.

To identify the ideals and parameters a person uses to compare her body to, first there must be *an understanding of what body image is.* The traditional understanding of body image is that it is a mental image in your mind of the body you want, typically represented by what others see as positive. With body image, typically the way the body is seen, whether positive or negative, is used to define the worth of that person. If people like the condition of your body, you are a more valuable person. If people don't like your body, you are a less valuable person.

The idea is that a positively seen body reflects a positive inner-self. It's as though the body—its function, abilities, its looks, and opinions about it—can be used with symbolism to define our intrinsic value as a human, as well as the quality and character of people we are. In order to form a body image in the mind, first there must be a parameter, or set of parameters that are believed to be ideal, from which the body is compared to. These ideals are dogmatic—set in place by some authority, unquestionably defining and promoting what they believe is superior for people to aspire for and to achieve.

For many people the ideal is a long and lean picture of thinness, where bones are visible, which is represented by the models in fashion magazines or seen on the runway. Some people idealize the fitness body with muscles and ultra-leanness that shows muscular definition and strength. Others seek the ideals of beauty defined by larger breasts, a small waist, and a large butt. They often also idealize make-up and accentuated lips and eyelashes.

No matter what the parameters of their chosen body-image ideal, the idea is the same: *when you achieve the ideal you are a better, more valuable and superior human.* **For this reason, when a person believes and internalizes a body image, she assumes that when she reaches the goal, she will feel better about herself.**

It could be a smaller waist, a lower weight, a specific size of clothing, or fitting into an old pair of jeans she used to be able to wear. It could be a certain amount of time on the treadmill, or an ability to do a specific number of pull-ups. Whatever the ideal, there are parameters used to measure how her body compares. When a person gets closer to achieving these parameters, she can experience a sense of accomplishment, or confidence. Some thinks she needs these accomplishments to improve her self-esteem.

Many people confuse self-esteem with body image. Because body image is assumed to be a direct reflection of your quality as a person, people think they are confident in themselves when they reach these standards. The truth is that they aren't confident in themselves, but are instead confident in the body image they're complying to. This isn't "self"-esteem but rather "body-image"-esteem.

I've had many clients feel at peace with their body at a larger than socially accepted weight. I've also had clients whose body matches the ideal ultra-lean body image who are severely ashamed with minor weight increases.

The discontent a person has with her body isn't just measured by the difference between what she has and what she wants, but it is also magnified by the importance, need, and strictness of how she holds herself to the ideal.

Ask yourself:

- What are your body image parameters and ideals?

- Describe the picture in your mind of the body you want?

- Where and who did you learn these ideals from?

- What would change in your life if those parameters and ideals no longer applied to you?

> # OBJECTIVE 2:
>
> **Identify beliefs and symbolisms attached to these body-image parameters.**

The confidence people attach in their mind to achieving the ideal body image is based on symbolism. These parameters are given meaning as if to non-verbally communicate, or give a hint about, a person's inner quality or worth. It's as if the way a person looks can tell you if she is a safe or risky person. Body image is used to make assumptions about a variety of human qualities and risks.

After years of study, here are some of the commonly discussed qualities of what thinness symbolizes, and consequently what being fatter symbolizes:

QUALITY	THINNESS	FATNESS
☐ Work ethic	Works hard	Lazy
☐ Intelligence	Smart	Dumb
☐ Cleanliness	Clean	Dirty
☐ Trust worthiness	Honest	Dishonest
☐ Sexuality	Sexual	Abstinent
☐ Health	Healthy	Diseased
☐ Physical	Comfortable	Uncomfortable
☐ Ability	Unlimited	Limited
☐ Emotional strength	Strong	Weak
☐ Dedication	Focused	Distracted
☐ Reliability	Reliable	Unreliable
☐ Resilience	*Can* handle challenge	*Cannot* handle challenge
☐ Kindness	Critical	Loving
☐ Lenience	Strict	Laid back
☐ Fun	Stick in the mud	Fun!
☐ Loving	Judgmental	Forgiving

In general, a narcissistic culture that promotes thin(ner) supremacy believes being thinner is associated with higher quality, and being fatter with lower quality. Even though people who have more body fat tend to be viewed as easier going, more loving, and more fun, there is stigma attached to having more body fat that when it's internalized can negatively impact how a person feels about herself.

Stigma is having a bad reputation, disgraced, or looked down upon for having some negative quality. Stigma assumes the person, as a whole being, is inherently a lower quality or defective. With that in mind, when a person believes in body-image dogma, and fears the resulting stigma for not complying, it would be understandable why a person would assume that by losing weight, she would feel better about herself. However, why aren't people questioning the stigma? Is it really true?

In order to question the stigma, you'd have to question the dogma that defines what the truth is. *Dogma is an unquestionable truth given to you by an authority.* In this case, the dogma is given to you by a thin-supremacy cultural belief that thinner people are better people. Similar to other narcissistic belief systems, like white supremacy, this belief system assumes that thinner people are superior people and therefore, fatter people are inferior. With dogma, you are *not* to question whether what they say is true. Therefore, if you are fatter, you have no choice but to think your body isn't good enough, and to battle your weight in order to feel better about yourself socially.

> **The truth is that there wouldn't be negative inferior attachments to fatness if there weren't positive, narcissistic symbolism attached to thinness.**

From there, the body is compared to the thinner/superior look held in your mind. The difference or similarity between what is idealized and what a person actually has, promotes a spectrum of either pride or shame attached to her body. *Once someone has internalized a body-image belief, it then becomes un-noticeable—like brainwashing. What is noticed, however, is how it makes her feel about herself.* When her body more closely matches the ideal image, she feels safer and more confident. When her body is further away from the ideal image, she feels insecure and vulnerable.

Most people are totally unaware they are identifying their worth and value based on symbolic body images, especially when their family and friends are doing the same.

- If your mother values her thinness and promotes food restriction, you will too.

- If she feels ashamed about her weight, and perpetually talks about how bad she feels about eating, you will too.

- If you hear others being constantly criticized or praised based on their looks, it will be internalized as important information that you should be aware of within yourself and others, *at all times.*

Many people wanting to lose weight are actually seeking the desire to feel lovable. Women have come to me seeking help with emotional eating— thinking they need to lose weight so that their husband will stop cheating. They think that by losing weight their spouse will love them more, or that losing weight will give them an opportunity to find a soulmate. They want to lose the negative stigma associated to having more body fat in order to achieve the positive benefits of what thin supremacy will bring them.

Body image symbolizes being lovable. For some people it is about getting others to love and appreciate her. However, for many of the clients I've worked with who suffered with the most excruciating shame and resulting eating disorders, it is about feeling lovable *to themselves.* They want to feel good in their mind about themselves, and without being thinner, they don't want to associate with their body. I believe this is a survival-mechanism directly tied to the need, as pack animals, to feel that we have something to contribute—*to feel that we are lovable.*

But if a person thinks her body threatens her lovability, she'll treat it like it's a threat. Despite the fact that her body is giving her life, consciousness, and all the senses that allow her to experience the world around her, she treats her body as if it's a predator threatening and destroying her life. She becomes a victim of her body, and her body is perceived as her persecutor.

In order to recover, a person must surrender the body image that has symbolized being lovable, but that has also defined her natural body as shameful and worthy of isolation. *This is the most excruciating and difficult part of recovery.*

OBJECTIVE 3:

Permanently surrender and let go of the symbolisms and benefits attached to the body image.

Giving up goals that symbolize acceptance, being loved, and the idea you'll be included isn't how our brain and instincts evolved. We evolved to do whatever we can to gain inclusion into our family and tribe as a way to secure our survival. "Fitting in" is the entire premise of Maslow's third hierarchy of need. Although, when the culture you are trying to assimilate into promotes body images that threaten and strain your psychological wellbeing—to the point you are suffering with an eating disorder—the only way to recover is to give up the security that body image apparently provides.

Once a person sees that her devotion and effort is far beyond what anyone should be expected to do in order to "fit in," she sees that her failure and inadequacy is worthy of compassion, understanding, and forgiveness.

Given the context of the unrealistic and inhumane standards of the thin(ner) supremacy belief systems, she doesn't deserve to live in shame or be defined by the suffering she lived while supporting that narcissistic cultural ideology.

Therefore, in order for a person to escape the controls of her eating disorder, it's inevitable she'll have to permanently surrender the symbolism of strength attached to her body image and eating, as well as all hope that she'll ever be thinner in order *to expose the weakness she feels within herself.*

When an eating disorder is what has kept you safe and hidden from exposure, letting go of the benefits attached to body image and the disordered eating can literally feel as if you're going to die.

By letting these standards and symbolisms go, you are essentially letting go of your survival. This must be accepted too. The risk of leaving the safety and predictability of a life you already know to then enter a new life you might be too weak to handle, and one you have no clue about—feels like suicide for many people.

Facing the exposure and terror without turning to a form of self-defense, even though you have no sense of strength to handle it, takes an incredible amount of humility and courage. The willingness to accept the truth, even when it comes with excruciating psychological pain, is a powerful act of faith, especially when there is no sense of what life will be like, or if you'll survive that pain.

If you are independently willing to humbly face, accept, and experience your inner sense of weakness as the truth of your capacity to handle life, no matter how pitiful and nonexistent it feels, the threats of not being lovable or not surviving lose their power. Once you've let go of body image and willfully faced rejection, abandonment, and a life being alone, you're going to have to redefine how you want to relate to your body and to life.

Ask yourself:

- Do you want to dislike your body?

- Do you want to have to change it before you allow yourself to start living?

- More importantly, what is the true genetic predisposition of your body if you were to completely stop all dieting, exercise, and emotional eating?

- Are you willing to find out the true nature of your body, even if it doesn't match what is culturally accepted?

OBJECTIVE 4:

**Accept the body unconditionally,
for what it naturally is.**

The goal of the fourth objective is to unconditionally accept whatever that body is. The only way you will be free from having to fix your body is if you accept the body for what it truthfully is, and stop altering it with some form of disordered-eating behavior.

This means you would have to accept what happens if you 1) stop excessively exercising, 2) stop counting calories or measuring your food, 3) stop reading food labels, 4) stop eating to escape uncomfortable emotions, and 5) stop any form of justified or reasoned restrictions or eating in excess.

There are five ways the body must be accepted in terms of thin(ner) supremacy:

1. You must accept that you'll never again be thinner than you are.

2. This requires you accept the current state of your body.

3. You must accept that your body might gain body fat and naturally be larger than the cultural ideal or what is deemed "healthy."

4. If your body is naturally thinner, you must be indifferent about it, without attaching pride or narcissistic value to it. This doesn't mean you can't notice or appreciate physical relief that occurs for some people with weight loss, but that you don't internalize it as a symbol of your worth. One way to think about this is that you are committing to never use your body as a means to supply love or inclusion in any relationship. In other words, you'll never put weight loss or thinness on your resume. You don't want your body image to be how you secure relationships with others. Even if you're given praise or compliments on your body, the goal is that these opinions, whether positive or negative, don't impact how you relate to your body.

5. If your body naturally loses weight, you must be willing to regain that weight. This means any natural unintended weight loss can be naturally regained, so don't attach emotion, pride, or shame to any of it.

The goal is *total indifference to your natural body size, shape, and weight.* If you gain weight, no big deal. If you lose weight, so what? If your body stays the same, that's okay too.

None of it matters, and all of it is good if that's what the body naturally does without forceful influence from bingeing, emotional eating, excessive exercise, dieting, or any imposed efforts to lose weight.

OBJECTIVE 5:

Agree to independently navigate the vulnerability and freedom in your life that arises after the body image, dieting, and emotional eating is let go.

Instead of hiding and fighting in self-defense, recovery requires you to accept the truth about yourself in exchange for freedom, even if it is seen as inferior. This freedom allows you to experience life from a new perspective—to see that your authentic value and ability to live isn't made better or worse when praised or judged by others when you're compared to self-"concepts" defined by a narcissistic culture.

The courage it takes to independently accept one's true self is the foundation of self-confidence, which opens the mind to curious wonderment, creativity, innovation, and exploration in life. Because the pressure to perform, please others, and to succeed at all cost is gone, the truth of one's capacity in life can be discovered and set free to flourish. With open mindedness, there is no need to control the outcomes of life, which means there is more willingness to take risks. It is at this point that a person transcends the crippling forces of survival mode to experience a different liberated way the mind works. Even though you have no sense of what will come to be, a new existence presents itself. It is free, open, and hard for many people to describe.

When freedom arises, the goal is to take the reins to independently define the worth of your life, and what you want out of it, even when you might feel too immature and weak to know what you want or like. You'll need to accept the truth about what you want out of life, even when others might not agree with it, without thinking there's something wrong with you or feeling bad about it. Moving forward, you'll need to take responsibility for expressing the nature of your true self, and make decisions for what is right and truthful to you.

Taking ownership of your life comes with freedom and infinite possibilities, no different than a toddler starting life from the beginning. Just as a young child learns the ins-and-outs of life, no matter what age you are when you choose independence, you too must learn the ins-and-outs of who you are and what you want with the life you're living.

And just as a child will be criticized when he or she doesn't match societal dogmas, you too must be open to being judged, ridiculed, bullied, and rejected when you honor yourself over the body-image dogma from which you're seeking liberation from.

The good news is that you get to do this as an adult who already understands how the society you live in works, and what true and real dangers do exist. You don't have to start over as a child, or have to live through the awkwardness and misery of junior high and adolescence all over again to get to this place of maturity and freedom. You have enough knowledge and wisdom to navigate the culture we live in, without taking it as seriously.

One way to describe this is that you are living "in" society, not "of" society. This means you can adapt and assimilate into culture, but culture doesn't become who you are, how you identify yourself, or how you define yourself. This allows you to be a human anthropologist, and to adapt to an ever-changing life that is always evolving in order to continue to learn, grow, and create and recreate what you want as your life progresses.

The goal is to recognize that you have good integrity, and that you've always done the best you could with what you were aware of—and what you were aware of was to do what others told you. Now, you are aware that maybe this wasn't the best thing for you psychologically or emotionally.

Eating Without a Body Image or Diet

As the desires diminish that are driving the need to lose weight and prevent weight gain, a person emotionally relaxes about food. Then her priority is to learn the sensations of hunger and fullness, and to distinguish the physical need for food from emotional desires to eat or diet. This often leaves people at a loss for how to eat and relate to food.

They previously related to food with such an emotional charge that eating was never about physical need. *Eating had been either about punishment or reward.* To have a neutral relationship with food can feel foreign and vulnerable. Many people describe this freedom with food as juvenile, or elementary—as if they are learning to live again, like the fresh start of a child. At this point, hunger and fullness becomes an important securing aspect of the body that guides the physical need for food. This is very different than the mental controlling-ness that diets previously imposed on the body.

The ability to identify the inherent sense of hunger and satiety, and the ability to discern psychological hunger from physical hunger, is fundamental for living free of dieting, deprivation, and emotional eating. When the hunger and fullness scale is truthfully followed, a more dynamic, adaptable, and functional way of eating—one that requires minimal effort can be experienced—especially when there is no famine, scarcity, or feelings of badness attached to food. This is the premise of the "Body" of the Mind:Body Method.

Part 2

The "Body" of the Method

Tackling Emotional Eating with the Hunger and Fullness Scale

The "Body" of the Method:

Addressing body image is foundational to providing a relaxed environment that is pivotal when learning and applying the hunger and fullness scale to guide when and how much to eat. As well, discerning and *truthfully* following the body's rhythms of hunger and fullness are very important in order to break emotional habits with food and dieting that formed as a consequence of body image and dieting.

The "Body" objectives of the Mind:Body Method are an approach to eating that reacquaints an individual with her body's natural regulation of hunger and fullness, without the stress and anxiety of having to control her size, weight, and perceived "health." The idea is to allow the body to do that job, and you then follow its lead. You allow the body to guide when and how much you should eat.

This is similar to how we allow the body to regulate when and how much we urinate. We don't necessarily tell the body to urinate on a schedule, and then monitor the chemicals and toxins released from the body, or tell the body how much total urination that should occur in a day. Why not give the body a similar freedom to regulate when and how much we eat?

The goal of this process is to first learn how the body signals and regulates the need for food, and second, to identify eating that is based on emotional needs that have nothing to do with physical need. Ultimately, as a person relaxes and allows her body to lead in guiding when and how much to eat, she will be free from regulating diets and mentally judging food that directs how to eat, and free from relating to food in a dysfunctional way as emotional support.

While this is done, she also completely stops all forms of strenuous exercise.

NOTE: Because strenuous activity is commonly used as a "purge" or a way to mask emotional eating, it is very important it is stopped long enough for a person to allow her natural body to reveal itself. During the recovery process, it's okay to do gentle yoga (non-heated), walking, and other non-strenuous activity that won't drastically impact energy needs and hunger rhythms.

The "Body" objectives of the Mind:Body Method are to:

1. Identify stages of physical satiation or complete fullness.

2. Identify states of physical hunger.

3. Differentiate mental hunger from physical hunger.

4. Identify triggers that prompt mental hunger and emotionally validated eating.

5. Allow discomfort without justification or action.

6. Eat based on physical need, reconditioning functional eating in uncontrolled situations.

OBJECTIVE 1:

Identify states of physical satiation or complete fullness.

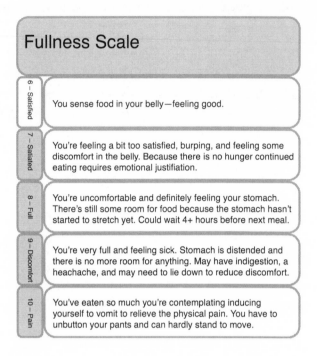

Fullness Scale

6 – Satisfied
You sense food in your belly—feeling good.

7 – Satiated
You're feeling a bit too satisfied, burping, and feeling some discomfort in the belly. Because there is no hunger continued eating requires emotional justifiation.

8 – Full
You're uncomfortable and definitely feeling your stomach. There's still some room for food because the stomach hasn't started to stretch yet. Could wait 4+ hours before next meal.

9 – Discomfort
You're very full and feeling sick. Stomach is distended and there is no more room for anything. May have indigestion, a heachache, and may need to lie down to reduce discomfort.

10 – Pain
You've eaten so much you're contemplating inducing yourself to vomit to relieve the physical pain. You have to unbutton your pants and can hardly stand to move.

On the fullness scale, this would be identifying 6, 7, 8, 9, and 10. Clearly differentiating a 5 from a 6 is imperative in relearning what it means when food is no longer needed hormonally, and when to stop eating (no matter how much food you are served).

Relearning to understand hunger signals and physical signs of satiation (removed from an emotional drive) is an integral part of eating based on the truth of the body's need for food. For people who are compelled and conditioned to eat based on emotions or strict adherence to rules of a diet, *fullness is either linked to shame resulting in an emotional binge, or its linked to a sense of security and freedom from the rigidity of the diet.* The goal here is to learn what these sensations feel like without some emotional judgment attached to it.

When a person is first learning to eat based on the rhythms of hunger, it's very common she doesn't recognize when she's had enough to eat until she is too full. It's important a person knows she hasn't done anything wrong. Initially overeating is understandable and expected, and its imperative people don't feel guilt or shame about it. This is what makes the process of learning safe, so that she can be truthful about how she is discerning her body. As well, this initial phase is when most people learn how these uncomfortable physical sensations feel, without being influenced by efforts to repress feelings of badness.

For some people learning to eat without rigid rules about food, the physical sensations of hunger are very intense, thus they have difficulty feeling satiated or even full. This too is to be expected when a person is allowed to eat food she's been withholding and hasn't learned to eat yet. For some people, they've denied themselves access to certain food for years. It's expected they will want to consume these foods first, and are likely to over-consume these foods. *This is a good thing*, and its important a person allows herself this freedom without guilt.

As a person continuously gives herself permission to eat foods that she's denied for long periods of time, eventually the fear that 1) its going away or 2) there isn't enough, will diminish. She also learns it isn't the type of food that makes her feel bad as much as eating too much of that food makes her physically uncomfortable. Not to say that some people have negative physical reactions to certain foods, but that it is more a function of timing and quantity.

As all food is allowed, it's imperative there is no judgment about the food and no "health" judgments about how much and how often it is eaten. If there's internal criticism about the food or thoughts that eating it is "bad" judgment, a person will experience anxiety and fear of the food, making it almost impossible to discern the signals of hunger and satiation. When food is eaten judgment free, it is much easier to discern these physical signals, and now the process of learning the body and its response to food can progress. As it sinks in that *all* food is safe and secure, the impulsive drive to overeat will subside.

Start the process with total permission to eat all food on the "table of abundance" as if each type of food is equally important and equally available all of the time, with nothing but your body's sensation of satiation to stop you.

OBJECTIVE 2:

Identify stages of physical hunger.

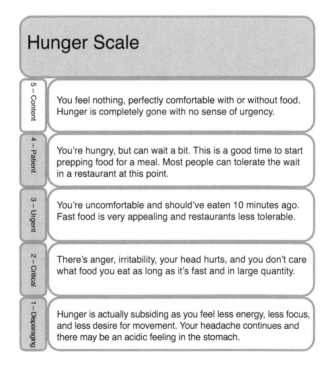

Hunger Scale

5 – Content	You feel nothing, perfectly comfortable with or without food. Hunger is completely gone with no sense of urgency.
4 – Patient	You're hungry, but can wait a bit. This is a good time to start prepping food for a meal. Most people can tolerate the wait in a restaurant at this point.
3 – Urgent	You're uncomfortable and should've eaten 10 minutes ago. Fast food is very appealing and restaurants less tolerable.
2 – Critical	There's anger, irritability, your head hurts, and you don't care what food you eat as long as it's fast and in large quantity.
1 – Disparaging	Hunger is actually subsiding as you feel less energy, less focus, and less desire for movement. Your headache continues and there may be an acidic feeling in the stomach.

Using the hunger scale, urgency to eat is identified using numbers 1, 2, 3, 4, and 5. This range of hunger goes from feelings of nothing (5) to complete loss of concentration, irritability, and painfully intense hunger (1). Clearly understanding the difference between 3 and 4 is critical in relearning the communication hunger provides as a signal for when the body needs food hormonally and when to start eating.

Many people have never felt hunger. In fact, it is not uncommon for people to think that hunger is when they no longer feel full. On the other hand, some people have learned to associate hunger with fear, or power, or control. The goal here, similar to discerning fullness, is to detach any emotional meaning or symbolism from the sensation of hunger. Relearning to recognize these physical signals along with the true feelings of hunger is also vital in relearning to eat and gaining independence from the rigid concepts defined by a diet and justified emotional eating.

> # OBJECTIVE 3:
>
> ## Differentiate mental hunger from physical hunger.

The more aware you are of your body's physical cues of hunger and sensations of fullness, the more obvious emotional justifications to control food and eating become—whether it's eating when you have no hunger, trying to eat less than the body needs, or continuing to eat after hunger is gone. What I love about this concept is that it's completely individualized and tailored to your body. This eliminates judgment towards both food and rules that are difficult to apply.

During the process, mental hunger becomes clear as the rules are less about weight and more about identifying habits, emotions, and dysfunctional ideals centered on eating, dieting, and food. When physical hunger is clearly defined (as emotional drive is removed), mental appetite and hunger are distinguishable and brought to the forefront of consciousness. This allows people to choose to evaluate where the desire to eat is coming from and to face what needs to be addressed, and to choose not to eat when there is no physical need.

This can occur not only before a person eats, but often after a person starts eating. She can be hungry when she starts eating, but as hunger subsides and sensations of satiation and fullness appears, the desire to eat for emotional reasons can arise. Deciphering the urge to reason, rationalize, justify, and argue for food occurs as it is clear the body no longer needs food.

OBJECTIVE 4:

Identify triggers that prompt mental hunger and emotionally validated eating.

Some people know exactly why they eat, but they may not realize why it's emotionally rationalized. These are the triggers that create mental appetite, emotional hunger, and feelings that food is needed.

For most, eating compensates for feelings of insecurity that is created by doubt in their ability to handle emotions independently without food. I've observed that these impulses often stem from feelings of being powerless, or from being a victim to some experience. Whatever the trigger, if there is no physical need, the mental hunger requires some form of validation to justify giving in to the dependent feeling.

Once hunger and fullness are recognizable, and the urge to justify dieting or overeating is clear, the goal is to do nothing in order to create a new perspective that gives people the confidence to process emotions independently—without food or the impulse to diet. This approach motivates people to open their minds to vulnerability—in order to intentionally test emotional independence.

OBJECTIVE 5:

Allow discomfort without justification or action.

For many, the emotional insecurity that brings about vulnerability feels unbearable. Letting go of an eating and dieting behavior that has felt emotionally important and rewarding can be extremely frustrating.

During the process people should seek to understand how they would eat if there wasn't a food or a diet to control or rescue them. The goal is to invite vulnerable discomfort rather than to justify removing it. Instead of eating, they must learn to acknowledge their body is in control, and if you're hungry you will eat…but if you're not hungry you won't eat.

For this to work it is imperative you hold yourself responsible to tell the truth.

If you want freedom from disordered eating and dieting, you have to be willing to experience *whatever it was that you hid from with those behaviors.*

This concept is foreign for many people who've been codependent on some form of coping mechanism or aid—using emotional band-aids, pacifiers, and any object or behavior to change and distract from uncomfortable feelings. Removing dieting and food from helping to strengthen you emotionally requires initial feelings of weakness and temporary discomfort, but in the end this experience and internal reflection about it allows for a completely new perspective and a "rebooting" of the mind and body. The goal here is *to surrender all justifications to find one's truth.* It is to intentionally test emotional independence without eating or dieting.

OBJECTIVE 6:

Eat based on the physical need, reconditioning functional eating in any uncontrolled situation.

Once there's a new sense of emotional autonomy, it's important to test functional eating in the real world of abundance. Building confidence in one's ability to sense hunger and eat various types of food (in different environments) is vital in the process towards emotional independence. Functional application of hunger and fullness, when huge quantities of uncontrolled food options are available, is the ultimate physical and emotional success.

When there's no diet, no boundaries, and no clear rules about how to eat, people can lack confidence in their emotional strength. Avoiding vulnerability keeps them too weak to independently sense emotions, and removes the opportunity to learn to functionally enjoy food.

It's not that we shouldn't like or take pleasure in food, but that we should become skilled at eating without making diet controls or compensatory excessiveness the gratifying focus. There's deep satisfaction with the delights and taste of food—when it's functionally eaten without guilt or overcompensation for a lack of freedom, and when the body feels absolutely no symptoms of discomfort from fullness.

For this reason, I suggest people seek out vulnerability and emotional tests of independence. I encourage them to go out to restaurants, parties, and every social occasion possible to gain social confidence while surrounded by food and people eating and talking about dieting. It gives them a chance to retrain and recondition their habits, so dieting and overeating is not the center of their life, entertainment, emotions, or their happiness.

The Objectives

The objectives of the "Body" of the Mind:Body Method are to reestablish a keen sense of hunger and fullness so that the body is given the power to dictate food consumption. When the natural guide to eat that we are born with is relearned—ignoring hunger and starving, as well as eating when the body has no hunger—becomes an obvious behavioral problem causing stress to the body. With the method, eating and dieting are seen as obvious emotional coping mechanisms that need to be addressed.

In summary:

- If there's focus on how the body responds in weight or size, unfortunately the hunger and fullness scale will become just another diet, set of rules, a daily battle with the scale, continued punishment for having to restrict, and the constant fear weight will be regained.

- As a result, hunger and fullness scale will be strictly reinforced with forceful perfectionism, ultimately promoting an all-or-nothing approach, as if it was a rigid diet.

- If the body is given the controls, and hunger and fullness is truthfully followed with the intent to end dieting and emotional eating.

- Then there's tolerance for emotional discomfort as old patterns of insecurity are independently secured.

The approach and purpose behind the hunger and fullness scale can either be to continue the weight-loss battle and the vicious all-or-nothing cycle between dieting and overeating, or end it completely. If approached with the intent to end dieting and emotional eating, then there's tolerance for discomfort as the body directs you how to eat through hunger and fullness, and as old patterns of insecurity are independently secured. On the other hand, if the focus is on how much weight is lost, the hunger and fullness scale will become another set of rules, a daily battle with the scale, continued punishment for having to restrict, and the constant fear that weight will be regained.

No matter how freeing eating to the biological rhythms of hunger is, it is your choice to follow it regardless of your size and weight. The Mind:Body Method holds participants accountable for a source of motivation that is not limited by a fleeting resolve for weight reduction. It exposes dysfunctional dieting, eating, and other compensations for insecurity, giving merit to authentic and genuine emotional strength. This process gives you an opportunity to break away from the codependent cycle between dieting and emotional eating, and freedom from the emotional limitations of both. The result is emotional strength and a body set free from the torments of overeating and dieting abuse.

Chapter 11

The Science of Hunger:
A "User-Friendly"
and More Scientific Explanation

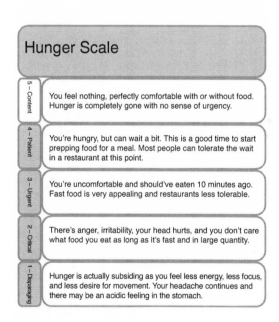

Hunger Scale

5 – Content
You feel nothing, perfectly comfortable with or without food. Hunger is completely gone with no sense of urgency.

4 – Patient
You're hungry, but can wait a bit. This is a good time to start prepping food for a meal. Most people can tolerate the wait in a restaurant at this point.

3 – Urgent
You're uncomfortable and should've eaten 10 minutes ago. Fast food is very appealing and restaurants less tolerable.

2 – Critical
There's anger, irritability, your head hurts, and you don't care what food you eat as long as it's fast and in large quantity.

1 – Disparaging
Hunger is actually subsiding as you feel less energy, less focus, and less desire for movement. Your headache continues and there may be an acidic feeling in the stomach.

"Inhabit the beauty that lives in your beastly body and strive to see the beauty in all other beasts."

– Cheryl Strayed, author

> **IMPORTANT:** : This first half of the chapter is a "user-friendly" explanation of hunger, expanding on the simpler version in chapter 8. The last half of this chapter was written for doctors, practitioners, and people who are formally educated in cell biology and physiology that might be interested in a more scientific explanation of hunger as well as use of the hunger and fullness scale. All sources and researched referenced are listed at the end.

The Science of Hunger:

A "User-Friendly" Explanation

Fat is An Organ

Leptin is primarily a fat-derived hormone. Since its discovery in 1994, the sciences of starvation, feeding, how the body uses fat for fuel, and obesity, have all exploded. Now that we know fat is an organ which can grow and deplete in significant size and cell count, our knowledge of how fat hormones function and influence other organs has completely evolved.

> **Today we understand leptin is a hormone that allows fat to be used for fuel, and it also transmits the message to the brain and throughout the body—that a person has sufficient fuel.**

As food enters the mouth and stomach, leptin is secreted into the blood stream. Although leptin comes from many areas of the body, the most significant amount comes from fat.

Because some people have more fat than others, this source of leptin can significantly influence flux in blood leptin levels, which causes other organs to over- or under-compensate. Excessive or insufficient amounts of body fat can directly influence the balance point of the endocrine system, and over time, can re-set the metabolic "set point" of the body. This incredible ability to adapt within the brain and organs, could present symptoms of organ damage, signs of physical distress, and disorder within the endocrine system.

The intense focus on leptin, fat, and our organ's hormonal reaction, has been the center of attention. Today science can now explain with confidence *leptin's role in sleep, ovulation, pregnancy, cardiovascular disease, Type II diabetes, Polycystic Ovarian Syndrome (PCOS), stress, inflammation, and more.* To stay focused on what is significant in eating to hunger, I will discuss only leptin's role with hunger, fat metabolism, fat gain, the thyroid, and stress.

Leptin: Hunger, Metabolism, the Thyroid, and Stress

As blood leptin levels rise, and leptin increases in the brain, the hunger center of the brain deactivates, communicating to the conscious mind that you have adequate fuel, which diminishes the urgency to eat. On the other hand, if leptin levels decline, the same hunger center senses a decline in fuel, and activates and communicates to the conscious mind an increased urgency to eat. Important: leptin only removes the urge to eat; it *does not* create fullness.

$$\uparrow \text{eating} = \uparrow \text{leptin} = \downarrow \text{hunger}$$

When restricting food while on a diet, there wouldn't be adequate leptin released from fat and other areas of the body to sufficiently deactivate this center of the brain. An obvious increase in the urge to eat would occur.

$$\downarrow \text{eating} = \downarrow \text{leptin} = \uparrow \text{hunger}$$

The difficulty here is in the interpretation of *hunger.* Hunger is too subjective in humans, especially with survival mode triggers. Many people eat without hunger before and after food restrictions, which can cause stress to this hormonal system. Take for example the difference in hunger between a person who has very little fat, compared to an individual with a very large amount of fat. Remember, the most influential source of blood leptin comes from fat, so how much fat a person has will absolutely affect how often she experiences hunger, and how much food is necessary to alleviate her urge to eat.

For example, a lean person might need to eat two apples to stimulate enough leptin from his or her small amount of fat to remove hunger in the brain. In comparison, an obese individual might need only half an apple to get the same amount of leptin, and the same relief from hunger.

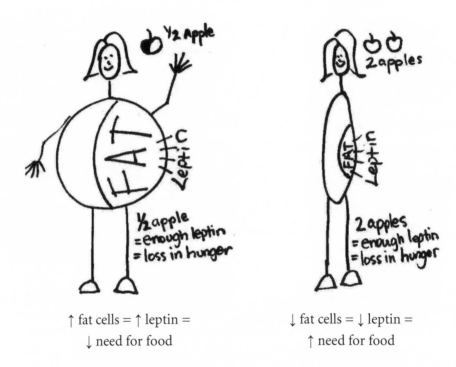

↑ fat cells = ↑ leptin =   ↓ fat cells = ↓ leptin =
↓ need for food   ↑ need for food

Leptin signals to the brain that the body has been sufficiently fed by alleviating hunger, but if the food that is eaten isn't digested, how could it possibly provide immediate fuel? What "feeds" the body while the food is still in digestion? To answer this, we need to discuss what leptin does to allow stored fat to be used for energy as the just-eaten food is digested.

As blood leptin levels rise while eating, fat cells begin metabolizing fat for fuel. Leptin opens access for fat to enter into the cell's mitochondria. The *mitochondria* is an organelle in each fat cell where the fat gets chewed up and spit out into the body as human fuel for muscles and organs. This immediate fuel availability energizes the functions of the body, and preserves blood glucose to be used in the brain.

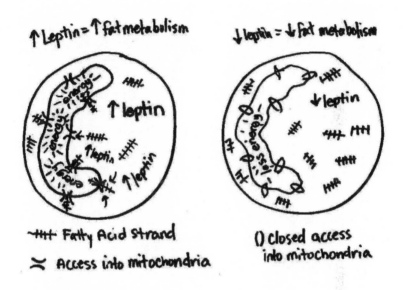

The immediate availability and conversion of fat into fuel provides what the body needs while food is digested.

- Could too much fat create a disproportionate breakdown of fuel, creating more than what's necessary?

- Could this create a backup or stockpile of fuel if it isn't used at the rate it's being produced?

- If so, could this cause a rise in blood glucose that would warrant the need for insulin to recreate fat out of the excess energy?

Unfortunately, large amounts of leptin seen in individuals with more body fat could be a sign of a variety of things. One sign might be they eat more than their body needs, or she is experiencing an environmental stress that stimulates too much leptin relative to the fuel she needs. In fact, the more leptin an individual produces, the more fat fuel she creates, and without equal demand, this causes an increase in the hormone *peroxisome prolifer-ator-activated receptor-gamma (PPAR-gamma)*, which is the master control switch for fat storage, controlling fat droplet formation and new fat cell maturation. These new fat cells show up in areas where you didn't have fat before, and are very difficult to lose. These areas of fat are highly associated with diseases such as Type II diabetes and heart disease—but without these new fat cells, you would not have enough fat to store the excessive produc-tion of fuel. This fat-gaining response aids both insulin and the liver by cre-ating new and bigger fat cells for the adequate storage.

However, these new fat cells can cause an even bigger problem because they can produce more leptin than normal-sized fat cells. This means they create more leptin when stimulated, and provide more fuel for the body. Each new larger fat cell magnifies the leptin-induced problem, and could cause ex-cessive fat-fuel production without warrant.

For example, compare a person who has only 10 pounds of fat to a person who has 100 pounds of fat. When they eat the same exact food (as food stimulates leptin), each cell of fat is stimulated to produce leptin, and then fuel. Thus, the person with more fat stimulates more leptin, and conse-quently more fuel than the person who has less fat cells.

> **This is why people who are very low in body fat tend to be hun-grier, and can also eat more without gaining fat, and why people who have significantly more fat are minimally hungry, and gain fat even when they eat very little.**

Each fat cell magnifies the function of this fueling system, so the amount of fuel a person gets is not measured by the food they eat, but rather by the amount of fuel their fat cells provide. Therefore, two people of different body fat can eat the same amount of food—and have a completely different fueling response. Simply put, the more fat cells you have, the less food you need to get appropriate amounts of leptin. The less fat cells you have, the more food it takes to simulate enough leptin to acquire adequate fuel for your body.

If an obese person eats two apples, his or her fat will provide fuel that is more than what was in the two apples she or he ate. This over-produced fuel requires a faster metabolism to balance fueling input with output, without gaining more fat.

$\uparrow$ fat + 2 apples = $\downarrow$ fat + 2 apples = energy balance
$\uparrow$ leptin = $\uparrow$ fat gain

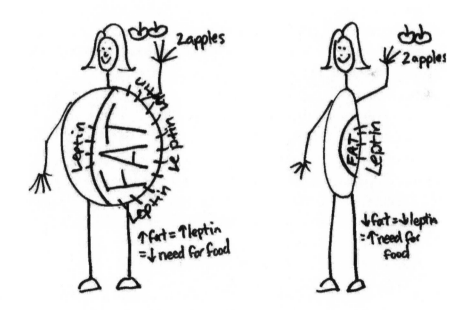

The amount a person should eat is not relative to how many calories she burns, but rather is relative to how much fat she has, and how much leptin her body produces, in relation to the environmental and psychological stimulus. Remember, fat isn't just a stockpile of energy, it is an organ that also coordinates with other organs. Therefore, if you have too much "fat organ" being hormonally stimulated, the other organs definitely are going to have to compensate. That is, unless the one conscious signal is used when leptin is too low or just right: *hunger*.

The convenient part about leptin is that when it declines, hunger is the result, and it's easy to know when eating is appropriate. Food and hunger are a perfect match because hunger results from lowering leptin levels, and food stimulates the body to make more. A person can individualize how much she should eat by 1) listening for this signal, 2) waiting for hunger to present itself, and 3) eating only enough for this hunger to confidently be satiated.

With the prior example, if the obese individual listens, he will notice his hunger diminishes after eating one half of the first apple. However, the leaner person with much less fat, will need to eat two apples to stimulate enough leptin to feel relief from hunger.

Simply put, if you're not hungry, your leptin levels are elevated, and your body is using stored fat as energy. If physical hunger increases, and the urge to eat is felt, then leptin levels are dropping, fat is insufficiently fueling the body, and the need for food is higher.

Thyroid, Energy, and Hunger

The body's response to starvation is triggered by the drop in blood leptin levels, which not only results in hunger, but also the suppression of the thyroid. As food is eaten, leptin stimulates the center of the hypothalamus that in turn controls the intensity of the thyroid signal. With a food-restrictive diet, when blood leptin levels fall, it would be appropriate to assume the thyroid signal would also weaken. This is a life-saving mechanism that weakens the body's energy system to sustain at a lower level, if fuel is not sufficiently supplied by reserves. This mechanism is like a light bulb that brightens or dims, using a dimmer switch. Leptin is the hormone that triggers the thyroid dimmer switch in the brain to turn up the signal, and energize the body.

↑ food consumption = ↑ leptin = ↑ thyroid signal = ↑ metabolic rate

↓ food consumption = ↓ leptin = ↓ thyroid signal = ↓ metabolic rate

Not only does leptin influences hunger and fat metabolism, it also affects the intensity of the thyroid signal, which controls the basal metabolic reaction of the body. Because leptin indicates to the brain and body there is sufficient fuel, a lack of leptin would signal insufficient fuel, consequently triggering the energy and fuel-conserving response to starvation.

With the increased demand on fat to create fuel for the body, the obvious result would be the removal and loss of excessive fat organ cells.

- As each fat cell depletes, less leptin would be stimulated, and the entire organ system of the body would be affected.

- Organs that were hyper-stimulated by leptin would get relief.

- Organs that were suppressed by too much leptin are now reactivated as leptin levels become balanced.

- With time and consistency, the entire hormonal system of the body would acclimate and create a new balance, optimally working with less leptin.

- The obvious result is an amount of body fat that works optimally with the rest of the organs in the body. This would effectively reduce risks of death and disease.

What we are dealing with is the hormonal system of the body, which is the entire endocrine system including the regulatory functions from within the brain.

> **IMPORTANT:** The content in this section is more scientific and was written for doctors and practitioners. If you are not formally trained and educated in cell biology and physiology, you can skip this section of the chapter.

The Science Behind Hunger:

A More Scientific Explanation

Energy Homeostasis (Balance)

To start, let's acknowledge the inherent difficulty of understanding the body's integrated system of organs, each requiring its own nourishment and energy demands, in addition to understanding the systems of tissues dependent upon these organs. The energy needed to sustain our organs and tissues is a system that feeds and depletes. It gives and takes from one organ to another, all while accommodating the complex influence from both physical activity and food. This balance of energy demand and energy sharing is called *energy homeostasis,* and maintaining homeostasis sustains these integrated systems during both feast and famine.

All systems integrate fuel and energy demands not only daily, but over a lifetime. This constant striving for homeostasis is what stimulates the feelings of hunger that prompt us to eat, and to stop eating when we're satiated. Perhaps the most critical element in achieving homeostasis is maintaining a stable blood-glucose level.

We are fed from many sources other than food; some sources of fuel are fat, muscle and liver glycogen, body protein, and blood glucose. These "tissue" fuels are not stocked equally. Some have more reserves than others. Fat and body protein by far surpass the fleeting amount of energy reserves held in both glycogen and blood glucose. The total integration of these fuel systems for short- and long-term metabolic homeostasis is vital to life, hourly, and over the period of our body's life.

The energy our body captures is powered not only by food, but also by our tissue reserves. However, these substrates must be converted into what can be captured before the body can use it as energy. As you eat, the food you consume is not yet in a form that can be captured as energy, so tissue reserves are readily available to meet immediate demands. However, for tissue reserves to be released, key hormones must be accessed that determine when and how much energy is needed.

Leptin is one of the most important energy-controlling hormones. Since its discovery in 1994, we more fully understand leptin's key role as a fatty acid synthase (FAS) inhibitor, and most notably as an anorexigenic hormone affecting the signal of hunger, the function of the thyroid, and fat metabolism.[4, 15]

Similar to insulin, leptin levels fall and rise in coordination with blood glucose, signaling to the body and brain when and how much energy reserve is available.[5] Leptin helps maintain blood glucose levels by regulating fatty acid use in skeletal muscle for energy, and preserving blood glucose for other more important organs to use.[5, 6]

Leptin is primarily found in white and brown fat cells, but could also be produced in the mouth, placenta, ovaries, skeletal muscle, stomach, mammary cells, bone marrow, pituitary, and liver.[6, 7, 8] The rise and fall of leptin levels influences hunger, thyroid stimulus, fat metabolism, and fat gain.[5]

Leptin and Hunger

As a diet begins, and food is restricted, blood glucose levels fall. As blood glucose levels drop in the body and brain, leptin also depletes.[9, 12] As leptin levels fall, there is a reduction in malonyl-CoA, a recognized intermediate, in the hypothalamic-signaling pathway that controls feeding behavior and energy expenditure.[13, 15] Recent evidence suggests that food deprivation, and the associated decrease in hypothalamic malonyl-CoA, increases the expression of neuropeptide Y (NPY) and agouti-related protein (AgRP), which produces the sensation of hunger. Conversely, as blood glucose and leptin levels rise after eating, the resulting increase in malonyl-CoA reduces the expression of NPY and AgRP, producing feelings of satiety when hunger is alleviated.[7, 10, 12]

Studies have shown that administering a fatty acid synthase (FAS) inhibitor (such as leptin) to the central nervous system in obese mice, dramatically reduces feeding behavior, with the increase in hypothalamic malonyl-CoA concentrations.[13, 21] These findings show that during very low-calorie diets, a stimulant of a FAS inhibitor like leptin, would raise malonyl-CoA levels, and decrease the expression of NPY and AgRP. Theoretically, this should sustain feelings of satiation for longer periods of time with less food.

Leptin and Fat Mobilization

Leptin is primarily expressed and secreted by fat cells. As fat mass increases during energy surplus, blood leptin increases and interacts with its receptors in the central nervous system (CNS), leading to increased malonyl-CoA expression in the hypothalamus, and decreased hunger.18 Although there could be fat loss due to lack of hunger with a FAS inhibitor, studies have shown central administration of FAS inhibitors transmitted to the skeletal muscle from the CNS, increases fatty acid oxidation and, with time, increases resting-energy expenditure.[16, 19]

As FAS inhibitors increase in skeletal muscle, the result is a decrease in malonyl-CoA. This outcome essentially determines whether or not fat is used for energy. 6 Muscle malonyl-CoA is a potent allosteric inhibitor of muscle carnitine palmitoyltransferase (CPT-1). CPT-1 is like a doorway on the mitochondrial membrane, opening or shutting access for fatty acids to enter and be converted into energy for the body. When CPT-1 is deactivated by muscle malonyl-CoA, entry of fatty acids into mitochondria for beta (ß)-oxidation is inhibited.[15]

Muscular malonyl-CoA formation is catalyzed with increased activity in the enzyme Acetyl-CoA carboxylase (ACC). ACC is strongly inhibited by AMP-activated protein kinase (AMPK), which is stimulated by leptin.11 So, as leptin levels decrease, AMPK is deactivated, which activates ACC. ACC creates malonyl-CoA, which inhibits CPT-1, and thus reduces fatty acid oxidation.[13, 15]

This happens as a response during starvation when blood glucose and leptin levels fall, preserving fat for longer periods of time, and forcing muscles to use other tissue substrates instead.[12] However, eating has the opposite effect.

After eating, when blood glucose and blood leptin levels increase, the activation of AMPK deactivates ACC, which decreases muscular malonyl-CoA. As muscle malonyl-CoA declines, CPT-1 activates and opens access for fat into the mitochondria, where energy can be supplied through ß-oxidation.[6, 11] This might explain how eating food that is not yet in a form that can be captured as energy, stimulates the use of stored fuel for immediate use.

New science has shown that this system can be successfully manipulated, not only to counteract symptoms of starvation, but to improve metabolic rates. Centrally administered FAS inhibitors during food restriction, rapidly increases the expression of skeletal muscle peroxisome proliferator-activated receptor- (PPAR), a transcriptional activator of fatty acid oxidizing enzymes, and uncoupling protein 3 (UPC3), a putative thermogenic mitochondrial uncoupling protein.[19, 15] Daily administration of FAS inhibitors over time increases the number of mitochondria in white and red skeletal muscle. This could explain why studies show increases in metabolisms tested through indirect calorimeter.[19, 22, 23]

This evidence shows that if there was a way to safely increase a FAS inhibitor such as leptin, as well as create energy demand with food restriction, the response over time should be to acclimate with more mitochondria, resulting in a higher caloric-burning capacity. However, without an FAS inhibitor, one should expect with the same food restriction to see a slowed loss in fat, increased loss of lean tissue reserves, and a resulting decline in resting energy expenditure.

To prevent the natural decline in fat mobilization with a very low-calorie diet, there must be an alternative way to stimulate leptin to decrease muscular malonyl-CoA. This allows fatty acids to have continuous access into the mitochondria, where fat could provide substantial energy for the body without significantly depleting blood glucose. This optimized fat utilization would prevent the need for the body to use lean tissue reserves during extreme caloric deficits and, over time, stimulate mitochondrial biogenesis, ultimately increasing the rate at which a person burns energy fuel at rest.

Leptin and Fat Gain

High levels of leptin in adipose tissue, without equally sufficient expenditure, have the opposite effect. Studies show that extremely high levels of leptin, similar to those seen in people who are considered obese, increase peroxisome proliferator-activated receptor-gamma (PPAR-gamma), which is the master control switch for fat storage.[17, 18, 14]

PPAR-gamma activates a host of enzymes that promote the esterification of fatty acids to create triacylglycerides (TAG), and advances the formation of lipid droplets from these TAG. When administered to mice, high levels of leptin increased the cellular expression of PPAR-gamma by 70–80 percent.[14] Leptin signals to the brain that there's ample energy in storage, but also forewarns pre-adipocytes to make room for more fat cells.

The more fat a person has, the more leptin his or her body produces.[17] Essentially, if you compared two people who have the same exact metabolic rate, but extreme variance in body fat composition, their bodies would have a different response to the same food. If they ate the same exact amount and type of food, the more obese person would have much more blood leptin stimulated, due to her larger amount of body fat.

The excess amount of leptin, without equal excess energy expenditure, can cause an imbalance in energy homeostasis, making the body more sensitive to resulting fat gain as a need to recapture and compensate for the imbalance. Leptin's stimulus of PPAR-gamma would complement insulin as a survival mechanism to make room for more fat, aiding in the preparation for more energy storage cells as an adaptation for long-term energy homeostasis. A person with less fat would have less leptin, which might better complement her metabolic energy balancing system, thus making her less sensitive to fat gain—even when eating the same exact meal as a more obese counterpart. Hence, fat gain and loss aren't a linear function of calories eaten and expended because fat hormones, such as leptin, greatly influence energy homeostasis, and the body's resulting compensations.

Both the fat-preserving and fat-creating effects of leptin function in order to conserve fat during starvation, and to form fat when food is excessive. Leptin's fat burning and storing/preserving relationships seem to follow an "inverted-U" model. Leptin's fat-conserving functions are maximum with high and low levels, and its fat-burning functions are optimal in the middle levels.

If leptin is stimulated by an influence other than food—like at different times during menstrual cycles or menopause, when a person gets injured, is sick, or under stress—there might be less necessity for food and more sensitivity to over-stimulate leptin production. There are a variety of environmental stressors that have been observed to stimulate the production of leptin. Therefore, a person's hunger and need to eat and her sensitivity to food would change depending on the state of her body's survival protective mechanisms. This excessive stimulus of leptin relative to expenditure would cause an expression of PPAR-gamma and an increase in fat when relatively small amounts of food are consumed without hunger.

Leptin and Perceived Danger

Survival mode is hard-wired physiological, psychological, and behavioral mechanisms triggered by apparent insecurity to handle perceived, or actual dangerous threats. These perceived dangerous threats have been shown to stimulate the body's production of leptin.[25] Some studies of eating behavior after a laboratory stressor showed an increase in leptin production and predictably reduced snack consumption.[27, 28] However, with increased leptin in relation to stress, studies have shown an increase in dopamine neurotransmission. The capacity for leptin to influence stress-induced dopamine (chemical in the brain) function is important as pathological states and mood are an integral component to pleasure-seeking behaviors.[29, 30]

As well, studies show that women who had a higher stress-induced leptin response had more abdominal fat than others with similar stress—but who had less abdominal fat.[26] However, due to vast diversity and variance in genetics and the amount of body fat a person has that can impact these outcomes, the link between stress and leptin aren't yet conclusive.

Leptin and Thyroid Function

Leptin's elevation and depletion in the brain signals a fed or starved state, not only through hunger, but also through the metabolic suppression or stimulus from the thyroid. [9] When elevated, leptin stimulates thyrotropin-releasing hormone (TRH) that controls the release of thyroid stimulating hormone (TSH). TSH acts on receptors in the thyroid to promote synthesis and release of the thyroid hormones (T3 and T4), which increases the body's basal metabolic rate.[8] As blood glucose levels fall with very low-calorie diets, the depletion of leptin in the brain inhibits this cascade affect, resulting in a weaker metabolic signal from the thyroid.[9]

The natural drop in thyroid signal is an essential, life-sustaining mechanism that occurs during starvation. This mechanism slows down the rate at which the body needs fuel, thus preserving energy stores and life for a longer period of time. However, when leptin is administered during induced starvation, the thyroid signals stay strong.[10] If the thyroid signal stays strong, the body maintains a normal basal metabolic rate, and requires the same amount of fuel as if in a fed state.

Leptin and the Hunger and Fullness Scale

The hunger and fullness scale can be used as a conscious reference to understand leptin levels, as well as when the need to eat food is hormonally appropriate. The hunger and fullness scale helps people verbalize and discern the physical sensations the body signals in order to guide when and how much to eat. Recognizing the sensations of physical hunger and fullness allows a person to learn the difference between her body's physical need for food and her emotional desires to eat. Having an awareness of the difference between physical hunger and emotional hunger is an imperative step towards understanding the root beliefs and thoughts that promote the desire to eat when there is no hunger, or to eat beyond comfortable satiation.

To recover from body image and disordered eating that occurs as a result, tell yourself the truth, and honor *your body's signal of hunger*.

Simply put, the goal is to wait to eat until you are truthfully hungry, and to eat adequately so that hunger is confidently removed, avoiding physical discomfort. When hunger increases, your leptin levels are declining, and food, as a stimulant, is needed. As hunger subsides and leptin levels increase, food consumption is no longer appropriate. To follow hunger as a guide, you must be keenly aware how foods differently influence the speed and longevity of this signal. You can't compare—when, what, or how much others eat—to your body's needs.

You can't compare your body's rhythm of hunger to anyone else, as different types of food combined with how many fat cells you have, greatly influence the timing and need for food.

People who have no idea what real hunger feels like, find this difficult to understand, especially those who've lived their entire lives eating based on the dictation of diets or the need for emotional eating. Individually, you need to recognize hunger, and develop confidence that your access to food is abundant and secure so that pressure to eat relaxes.

Again, this brings us back to the hunger and fullness scale as a rationing guide, and trusting that your body knows exactly how much it needs, and when.

"If hunger is not the problem, then eating is not the solution."

– Author Unknown

Start by looking at the role that eating plays in your life. Ask yourself:

- Do I know what hunger feels like?

- When do I eat without hunger?

- How often do I eat until I'm overly full?

- How do I justify over-eating or eating without hunger?

- Could I stop eating when hunger goes away, no matter how fabulous the food tastes?

"A surrendered person can eat anything or go anywhere and is no longer subject to fears of contaminants, pollutants, drafts, germs, electromagnetic frequencies or food dyes. Our perception of the body shifts…This shift of perception is from 'I am the body' to 'I have a body.'"

– Dr. David R. Hawkins, *Letting Go: The Pathway of Surrender,* page 242

Chapter 12

In Conclusion

"You will learn a lot from yourself if you stretch in the direction of goodness, of bigness, of kindness, of forgiveness, of emotional bravery. Be a warrior for love."

– Cheryl Strayed, author

In Search of the Truth...Question the Way You Think and What You're Afraid of.

Most of what I do with people when they seek my help is to give them perspective. I'm doing nothing other than giving them a different vantage point to look at why they're doing what they're doing, so they can understand what they'll need to give up and let go of in order to be free from the behaviors they want recovery from.

Besides discussing theories on survival mode, Maslow's hierarchy of needs, evolutionary psychology, narcissistic cultural dogma, body image, and thin supremacy...I spend a great deal of time asking clients clarifying questions.

I know for me, when I believed the misery of my eating-disorder behaviors were inescapable, and subsequently I decided to end my life—as I prepared for suicide, there were questions that came to my mind. These questions specifically uncovered why I was clutching to the behaviors that defined the eating disorder. I sought to answer those exposing questions truthfully— even if the truth uncomfortably challenged my beliefs and my identity. My answers came from a place of humility, seeking understanding rather than a way to defend myself or justify the disordered survival behaviors I was killing myself with. Today, I try to do the same when I ask questions of the person who is seeking the same clarity.

However, at first some people give me answers that are based on impulse, based on their fears, and based on protecting and reaffirming their brainwashed body-image dogma. In those cases, I refuse their answer, because they aren't telling the heartfelt truth, nor will they escape if they continue to defend the abuse. Sometimes I have to ask the same question two to five times before a person actually thinks deeper, allows for their discomfort, and gives a truthful answer. When she gets past the mentally constructed answer to seek the truth from her heart and soul, she experiences what it feels like to be humble, to be vulnerable, and to be released from defending narcissistic aspects of the dogma.

The truth does set you free.

> **There is freedom and peace in facing the vulnerable truth to humbly admit complete and total failure, without blame, self-defense, or excuse. It means you are liberated from having to fight to prove otherwise, and permanently free from having to defend yourself from that threat.**

If you are wanting freedom from beliefs that shame you, behaviors that hurt you, and dogma that controls you, *ask yourself the questions you don't want to answer.*

✓ Be honest even if it hurts your fearful ego.

✓ Look at your life from a viewpoint that isn't comfortable.

✓ Have courage to tell the truth, to be alone if that's what the truth entails, and to take responsibility for navigating and directing the life you are living in a way that brings you joy.

✓ When you open yourself up to the truth, you are opening yourself up to forgive yourself, to forgive others, and to forgive the rigid rules that keep you confined.

✓ Living in grace with the truth gives you freedom and a life you will feel worthy of living.

Ask yourself and answer *truthfully*:

- How would your life change if all forms of dieting and weight loss were removed forever?

- What would change if you had to be 100 pounds heavier, for the rest of your life? No amount of exercise, dieting, or surgery could change it.

- If your true natural body is larger than the "ideal," would you willfully focus on dieting and restricting food for the rest of your life, to force your body to be thinner than it's supposed to be? Knowing that the focus on your weight would have to be permanent?

- What would happen to your eating disorder of you got in a car accident and permanently lost the use of your legs? If you lost your eyesight? Lost your hearing? Your entire face and body got burned in a fire and you are permanently disfigured and scarred? Etc., etc.

- If it meant *permanent* freedom from having to fixate on food, focus on restriction, being obsessed with your body, and ashamed and in fear of gaining weight, would you be willing to permanently agree to accept a larger body? Would you be willing to live the rest of your life and all of life's adventures in that larger body?

- What would happen to bingeing and emotional eating if there were no diets, no food judgments, no food guidelines, no "good" or "bad" foods, no "you should eat less" statements, and no concept of "health" attached to food?

- If you won the "food lottery" and was awarded freedom from all food criticisms and judgments and awarded all of the food you could imagine from all over the world, to eat at any time, in any quantity, for any reason, forever— would you continue to overeat or binge knowing the food will never go away? How would your relationship with food change?

- If God or your higher power came to you and said:

  "You are free from ever having to care about your weight. *Fixing your body wasn't supposed to be your purpose in this life.* Whether you're fatter or thinner isn't what your life is supposed to be about! The more you focus on food, worry about your weight, and fix-ate on your size and health, the less freedom you have to live your life and to experience your true purpose. No matter what your weight and size, you are to stop caring about your body and your "health," and you are to open your mind to live this life *right now.* Noth-ing about your body needs to be fixed. Forgive your-self and move on. You are free to create a life that can change and evolve in a way so that you can experience life to the fullest, and when it's time for this life to end, you don't have to worry about that either."

  What would you do? Would you willfully choose to con-tinue to fixate on your body, your weight, food, and need-ing to diet? Or would you accept freedom and move on with your life?

- What would it feel like to accept that you've always done the best you could with what you thought was the right thing to do—even when you clearly made mistakes or made decisions that you regret? No matter what has happened to your body, to your relationships with people, and to your life—what would it feel like to recognize it is all understandable and completely forgivable? You realize that you and all of the people who might have hurt you are worthy of grace, forgiveness, and mercy.

In Conclusion

"Don't wait until everything is just right. It will never be perfect. There will always be challenges, obstacles and less than perfect conditions. So what. Get started now. With each step you take, you will grow stronger and stronger, more and more skilled, more and more self-confident and more and more successful."

– Mark Victor Hansen, author

Over the years, I've had the opportunity to observe full recovery from people who've suffered with eating disorders from all over the spectrum. I've also been able to witness continued struggles and frustration as people strain, while gripping onto their desires and wanting to be thinner and diet, as well as wanting to eat as an emotional coping mechanism. One of the greatest blocks in people's recovery is when they think freedom is an all-or-nothing process.

For some people, freedom comes to them permanently and abruptly. For others, it comes in waves because of the different stages of humility the process requires.

More often than not, escaping and recovery is a trial-and-error process of letting go—like a battered woman that leaves and then returns to her abuser over and over again. It takes *letting go to know freedom does exist, and for some people it takes a return to suffering to get clarity about the truth, and to accept what needs to be surrendered, faced, and accepted.* As people go back and forth between freedom and suffering, when they give themselves grace and wiggle room to figure it out, eventually they clearly see the lies of the fantasy, and they finally let it go completely. This is the point when their mind is free to explore life, and they've learned they don't need or want another captor that keeps them trapped in fear and self-defense.

What it takes for a person to eventually get complete and total freedom, and then recovery, is unique to her personal willingness to face her own mortality, and to accept that by giving herself grace to figure it all out, she can handle it.

With courage to stop defending oneself from threats of rejection and abandonment that trigger her third hierarchy of need, she is set free from the need that's defining and controlling her mind. With courage to face survival threats to her "health" and body that trigger her first and second hierarchies of need, she is released from being a servant to those fears. When fear of her own body and food loses its power, and the anxiety and pressure to micromanage food, diet, exercise, and concepts of "health" lose importance— the mind is set free to be more rational and balanced about caring for her body. By surrendering to the vulnerability of death, a person who previously was a slave to those survival mechanisms, is set free to determine for herself what's worth fighting and suffering for and what isn't. This is the space of openness and freedom that exists after you escape, as well as the rebirth and recovery of your truth.

This below quotation perfectly describes what I experienced once I escaped and then recovered. My hope is that you, too, can come out of the storm different than the person who walked into it.

"And once the storm is over, you won't remember how you made it through, how you managed to survive. You won't even be sure, whether the storm is really over but one thing is certain. When you come out of the storm, you won't be the same person who walked in. That's what this storm's all about."

– Japanese writer, Haruki Murakami

• • • • • •

Acknowledgments

I'd like to thank all the clients I've coached over the years who were willing to share their stories with the world on my YouTube channel. You are helping others by allowing them to witness your struggles and success in the process of recovery.

Next, I'd like to acknowledge and thank my copy development and line editor, Connie Anderson of Words and Deeds, Inc. Without her talents and the integrity of her work, I would have never finished this project, and it would've been far more difficult to read. Connie has been an imperative partner in capturing for the reader what I am trying to communicate. She is incredibly gifted and has been an essential influence to this body of work. Many people had told me that I'm a good writer—but my response is to let them know I have an incredible editor.

To the most talented graphic and concept designer, Katie Phipps. The cover design for this entire series and all of the Weight-Loss Apocalypse series is a work of genius. Katie, I feel like I won the lottery with your incredible talent guiding the visual identity of each book.

To Sue Stein, who designed the interior format for each book in this entire series. Thank you for your tireless work and willingness to go above and beyond to make each page work together seamlessly.

A special thank you to Denise Watson and Dr. Ed Hagen from Vivify Integrative Health in Hudson, Wisconsin. You gave me the opportunity to teach your patients, one by one, for years. Repeating the same explanation over and over, hundreds of times, was an invaluable part of refining how I teach the Mind:Body Method to participants. This work with you has been precious.

Thank you to my professors at Boise State University. Without such rigorous educational standards, I couldn't have understood the research that provided the basis for the content discussed in this book. To the Kinesiology department: Thank you for having such passion for the health of the human mind and body.

My hard-working and humble parents—for being the ultimate examples of perseverance and integrity. To my siblings—Steve, Laura, Daniel, Jennalee, Debbie, Becky, Melissa, Cliff, Katie, Mike, Big Jeff, Little Jeff, and Jean—for helping develop my "character."

References

(1.) Buss, David. (1995). Evolutionary Psychology: A New Paradigm for Psychological Science. *Psychological Inquiry.* 6: 1-30. doi:10.1207/s15327965pli0601

(2.) Kristin Neff, Ph D. (2015). *Self-Compassion: The Proven Power of Being Kind to Yourself.* William Morrow Paperbacks

(3.) Hawkins, David.R. (2018) *Map of Consciousness. Book of Slides (The Complete Collection) Presented at the 2002-2011 Lectures with Clarifications.* Pages: 12,104-107

(4.) Zhang, Y., et al. 1994. Positional cloning of the mouse obese gene and its human homologue. *Nature.* 372: 425-432

(5.) Morton, G.J. 2007. Hypothalamic leptin regulation of energy homeostasis and glucose metabolism. *Journal of Physiology.* 583.2: 437-443

(6.) N.Y. Ann. 2002. Regulation of fat metabolism in skeletal muscle. *National Academy of Sciences of the USA.* 967:217-235

(7.) Margetic, S., et al. 2002. Leptin: a review of its peripheral actions and interactions. *International Journal of Obesity.* 26: 1407-1433

(8.) Groschl, M., et al. 2001. Identification of Leptin in Human Saliva. *The Journal of Clinical Endocrinology & Metabolism.* 86(11): 5234-5239

(9.) Mars, M., et al. 2006. Fasting leptin and appetite responses induced by a 4-day 65% energy-restricted diet. *International Journal of Obesity.* 30: 122-128

(10.) Rosenbaum, M., et al. 2002. Low-dose leptin administration reverses effects of sustained weight-reduction on energy expenditure and circulating concentrations of thyroid hormones. *The Journal of Clinical Endocrinology & Metabolism.* 87:2391-2394

(11.) Flier, J.S., et al. 2000. Leptin, nutrition, and the thyroid: the why, the wherefore, and the wiring. *The Journal of Clinical Investigation.* 105(7): 859-861

(12.) Ahima, R.S., et al. 1996. Role of leptin in the neuroendocrine response to fasting. *Nature.* 382: 250-252

(13.) Kahn, M.Y. 2003. Role of AMP-activated protein kinase in leptin-induced fatty acid oxidation in muscle. *Biochemical Social Transactions.* 31(pt 1): 196-201

(14.) Flier, J.S. 1998. Clinical Review 94: What's in a name? In search of leptin's physiologic role. *Journal of Clinical Endocrinology and Metabolism.* 83(5):1407-1413

(15.) Wolfgang, et al. 2007. Regulation of hypothalamic malonyl-CoA by central glucose and leptin. *The National Academy of Sciences of the USA.* 104(49): 19285-19290

(16.) Qian, H., et al. 1998. Leptin regulation of peroxisome pro-liferator-activated receptor-gamma, tumornectrosis factor, and uncoupling protein-2 expression in adipose tissue. *Biochemical and Biophysical Research Communications.* 246(3): 660-667

(17.) Wolfgang, M.J., et al. 2008. Hypothalamic malonyl-CoA and the control of energy balance. *Molecular Endocrinology.* 22(9): 2012-2020

(18.) Orci, L., et al. 2003. Rapid transformation of white adipocytes into fat-oxidizing machines. *The National Academy of Sciences of the USA.* 101(7): 2058-2063

(19.) Considine, R.V., et al. 1996. Serum immunoreactive-leptin concentrations in normal-weight and obese humans. *The New England Journal of Medicine.* 334(5): 292-295

(20.) Friedman J.M., et al. 1998. Leptin and the regulation of body weight in mammals. *Nature.* 395:763-770

(21.) Cha, S.H., et al. 2005. Inhibition of hypothalamic fatty acid synthase triggers rapid activation of fatty acid oxidation in skeletal muscle. *The National Academy of Sciences of the USA.* 102: 14557-14562

(22.) Schwarts M.W., et al. 2006. Central nervous system control of food intake. *Nature.* 404: 661-671

(23.) Cha, S.H., et al. 2003. Hypothalamic malonyl-CoA as a mediator of feeding behavior. *The National Academy of Sciences of the USA.* 100: 12624-12629

(24.) Cha, S.H., et al. 2006. Hypothalamic malonyl-CoA triggers mitochondrial biogenesis and oxidative gene expression in skeletal muscle: role of PGC-1 . *The National Academy of Sciences of the USA.* 103: 15410-15415

(25.) Thupari, J.N., et al. 2002. C75 increases peripheral energy utilization and fatty acid oxidation in diet-induced obesity. *The National Academy of Sciences of the USA.* 99: 9498-9502

(26.) Konishi, N., et al. 2006. Systemic stress increases serum leptin level. *Journal of Gastroenterology and Hepatology.* 21(7):1099-102

(27.) Brydon L., et al. 2008. Stress-induced cytokine responses and central adiposity in young women. *International Journal of Obesity* (Lond), Mar;32(3); 443-450

(28.) Appelhans, BM. Circulating leptin moderates the effect of stress on snack intake independent of body mass. *Eating Behavior.* Aug;11(3): 152-155

(29.) Tomiyama, AJ., et al. 2012. Leptin Concentrations in response to acute stress predict subsequent intake of comfort foods. *Physiology Behavior.* Aug 20; 107(1):34-39

(30.) Burghardt, Paul R., et al. 2012. Leptin Regulates Dopamine Responses to Sustained Stress in Humans. *The Journal of Neuroscience.* October; 32(44); 15369-15376

After publishing *Weight-Loss Apocalypse* in 2011, author Robin Phipps Woodall started a YouTube Channel to share her coaching sessions that helped people who struggled to stop emotional eating. As Woodall met with each of her coaching clients, she found that her significant experience with an eating disorder, as well as her miraculous recovery, kept coming up in their discussions. For thousands of followers, Woodall's story was only understood through bits and pieces discussed in these YouTube videos.

In this book, Woodall tells how in the matter of a couple of years she went from being a cheerful college student to suffering with suicidal depression and a relentless eating disorder. While in a deep state of contemplation as she emotionally prepared to end her life, Woodall miraculously recovered. Not only did she experience an instantaneous removal from every negative aspect of the disorder and depression, but she also came out of it having a total shift in the way she perceived and lived life.

After over 20 years of being totally recovered, Robin Woodall is excited to tell you her story: *My Weight-Loss Apocalypse.*

After 8 years, author Robin Phipps Woodall has updated *Weight-Loss Apocalypse*, adding 52 pages of new mind-opening content. In the second edition, along with the important discussions of Dr. Simeons' hCG protocol, the need for further scientific investigation, and the hunger and fullness scale, Robin examines further the impact dieting has on emotional eating.

She explains: Until the influence that dieting has on over-eating or emotional eating is exposed as problematic, the demand for excessive amounts of food will continue, and weight gain will always be viewed as the problem. This additional discussion is instrumental in preparing the reader for the next book in the series: *Weight-Loss Apocalypse, Book 2,* which complements this book by addressing how body image negatively impacts how people approach Dr. Simeons' protocol.

For this reason, Robin is excited to present this updated second edition as *Weight-Loss Apocalypse, Book 1.*

"Robin has done it again. Whether you're new to the hCG protocol, or you've done the protocol more times than you'd like to admit this groundbreaking book is for you."

– Becky Sumsion, RDN, CD, Life Coach, Author

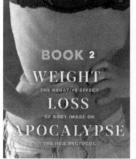

After over a decade of continued observation, author Robin Phipps Woodall is excited to share what she's discovered regarding the emotional impact of Dr. Simeons' hCG protocol. In *Weight-Loss Apocalypse– Book 2*, Robin examines the affect that negative body image has on a person's impulse to diet—and how repeated cyclical bouts of the hCG protocol done for this reason can be emotionally and physically harmful. Disarming beliefs that impel people to feel bad about their body is an essential step when approaching the hCG protocol, not as a diet, but as a serious medical treatment.

In this book, Robin describes the psychological risks of the very low-calorie protocol as well as the importance of an emotional evaluation, alongside a physical evaluation, in determining whether a person is an appropriate candidate for the hCG protocol.

For thousands of years, cultures have pushed physical ideas and concepts of the body as a way for people
to achieve superiority and success. Like foot binding
to make feet smaller, or the use of corsets to mini-
mize waist size, many of these body images result
in painful disability and disfigurement. Today the
"superior" body being pushed comes from ideas of
health and attractiveness as seen through images of
ultra-lean thinness. Author Robin Phipps Woodall
calls this "the culture of thin supremacy."

In *Thin Supremacy*, Woodall connects the individual's drive to achieve superior body images to human survival instincts, compelling people to fit in as
a way to be viewed as worthy of love and inclusion. Unfortunately, as images
of worth based on thinness have become more and more unrealistic, sadly
this is on the rise: people suffering from emotional issues stemming from
shame about their body. Woodall confronts the culture of thin supremacy—
and encourages the reader to question their beliefs about body image.

In this book, author Robin Phipps Woodall builds on the significant discussion of body image from her first book, *Thin Supremacy*. Here she expands further to explore the overwhelming—and sometimes traumatic or even tragic—impact that negative body image has on dieting and emotional eating.

From the viewpoint of evolutionary psychology, in *Diet Supremacy*, Woodall illustrates how fears of social stigma, based on body fat, trigger primitive survival mechanisms that motivate people to seek safety and control through forms of "diet supremacy." The toxic bond between negative body image and dieting while surrounded by abundance of food, promotes the angst and strain responsible for increasing one's feeling of deprivation. The result is an increase in cravings, perceived hunger, and the impulsive drive to eat excessively. This is an important topic every weight-loss business, dieter, emotional eater, and eating disorder specialist needs to know about, understand, and especially discuss with those affected.

In *Body Supremacy,* author Robin Phipps Woodall expands on her first book, *Thin Supremacy,* and her second book, *Diet Supremacy,* to describe how these narcissistic belief systems combine to form the foundation for an eating disorder to develop. From the perspective of her own amazing recovery, Woodall presents a discussion about eating disorders as a psychological syndrome stemming from mechanisms of survival. A person suffering with an eating disorder is fighting to survive, even though her defense mechanisms are in fact killing her.

This book would interest a reader who wants to study and understand a different point of view for why people hold themselves hostage inside the darkness of an eating disorder. If you are studying eating disorders, work with people who suffer inside the darkness of an eating disorder, or are suffering yourself, this most-informative book was written for you.

In *Surrendering Your Survival*, author Robin Phipps Woodall describes the perspective of living your life while coming out of the self-centered nature of survival mode that was previously controlled by "thin and diet" supremacy belief systems. When a person rejects those belief systems to instead accept herself unconditionally, survival mechanisms calm down, and her mind shifts open. As people are liberated from narcissistic body images and diet supremacy, they are left to question how they should eat moving forward.

For this reason, Woodall describes in *Surrendering Your Survival* the science of hunger and satiety, as well as how important these physical senses are when relearning how to eat without fear or shame. The goal is to renew your relationship with your body and food in such a way that they are not the focus of your life as you move forward. This leads to the glorious and life-saving freedom people experience when they are recovered.

FOR MORE INFORMATION

Website: *https://weightlossapocalypse.com*

Email: *info@mindbodyhcg.com*

YouTube: *https://youtube.com/user/weightlossapocalypse*

Instagram: *@WeightLossApocalypse*

Twitter: *@MindBodyMethod*

Facebook: *Weight-Loss Apocalypse*

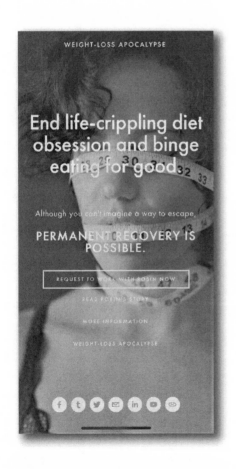